Decisi

A Mode

Volume 1

Decision Mathematics

A Modern Introduction

Volume 1

Robert Davison and **Lynda Cochrane**

Cranfield

British Library Cataloguing in Publication Data
Davison, Robert
   Decision Mathematics: A Modern Introduction
   1. Finite mathematics
   I. Title   II. Cochrane, Lynda
   510

ISBN   1 871315 30 1 net
         1 871315 31 X non-net

Produced by
Chase Production Services
for
Cranfield Press
Cranfield Institute of Technology
Bedford, MK43 0AL, UK

Printed in the United Kingdom

CONTENTS

PREFACE

It is now generally accepted that any undergraduate mathematics course should include a study of decision mathematics. It has for a long time been included in business courses; linear programming and critical path analysis, for example, are well established areas of such courses. These topics, together with several more, are included in *Decision Mathematics* which is aimed at business students in their initial years. Decision mathematics has been embraced by the computer scientist too, as algorithm design grows in importance. Design of efficient computer networks uses many of the ideas presented in these two volumes.

For many years calculus has dominated the VIth form and undergraduate curriculum, but in recent times the importance and applications of decision mathematics have been recognised. Course content is gradually changing to reflect this growing importance. The Decision Mathematics syllabus introduced by the Oxford Board has extended decision mathematics into the VIth form curriculum. *Decision Mathematics* covers all the subject areas of this exciting innovation and aims to show that decision mathematics is useful, powerful and interesting.

Volume 1 begins with a chapter on algorithms. The concept of an algorithm is central to *Decision Mathematics* with many of the topics being expressed in algorithmic form. Chapters 2 and 3 show how the classical transportation and assignment problems can be solved by application of suitable algorithms. Linear programming belongs to the core of decision mathematics and no book in that area would be complete without it – chapters 4 and 5 cover in detail both the graphical and simplex approach to the linear programming technique. Chapter 6 introduces game theory.

The idea of problem solving via algorithms runs throughout the second volume. Chapter 1 gives an introduction to graph theory and shows how various topological problems (for example shortest path, minimum connector) can be solved by suitable algorithms. Network flow problems are considered in chapter 2 and critical path analysis in chapter 3. An elementary introduction to dynamic programming is the subject of chapter 4 and this is linked to the first chapter. Determining the complexity of an algorithm often entails solving a difference equation so it is apposite that the volume concludes with a study of difference equations.

Each chapter contains exercises and fully worked solutions are given at the end of each volume.

1
ALGORITHMS

Introduction

Recent years have witnessed an increasing interest in the use of algorithms. *An algorithm may be described as a step-by-step set of instructions which when followed solves a problem.* At a very simple level, the sets of instructions on a packet meal or a tube of adhesive are examples of algorithms. (See Figure 1.1)

Algorithm to Prepare a Quick Setting Resin

Step 1   Squeeze out equal amounts of resin (blue tube) and hardener (red tube).
Step 2   Replace caps immediately; blue cap for blue tube, red cap for red tube.
Step 3   Mix the resin and the hardener.
Step 4   Now use the mix. (The mix will remain usable for up to 3 minutes.)

We shall list the properties of algorithms and then continue by studying algorithms in common use. As many algorithms are used in computer programs we shall adopt a programming style and present algorithms in a structured manner. Two processes for which many programs have been written are *searching* and *sorting*. Given a long list of data e.g. numbers or names, we may wish to search the list for a particular entry. Once found, the position of the entry would be noted. In the sorting process we are given a list and wish to arrange the entries in some particular order e.g. increasing or decreasing if the entries are numbers, alphabetically if the entries are names. This chapter includes examples of both searching and sorting algorithms. The chapter concludes by discussing the complexity of an algorithm. This gives a measure of how long the algorithm is likely to take when executed by a computer. To minimise time and costs, it is clearly desirable to write efficient algorithms.

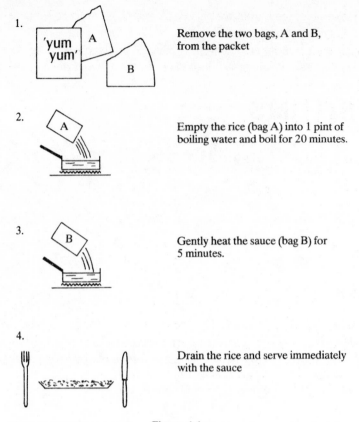

1. Remove the two bags, A and B, from the packet

2. Empty the rice (bag A) into 1 pint of boiling water and boil for 20 minutes.

3. Gently heat the sauce (bag B) for 5 minutes.

4. Drain the rice and serve immediately with the sauce

Figure 1.1

Properties of Algorithms

Some of the desirable properties of algorithms can be seen even from the very simple examples referred to in the introduction.

- Each instruction should be unambiguous. The algorithm must not be open to various interpretations.

- There can be only a finite number of instructions. This is obvious. If there were an infinite number of instructions to carry out we would never complete the problem.

- For a given input there should be a definite unique output when the algorithm has been executed.

For the meal example, the inputs are packets A and B. After following the instructions (algorithm) we obtain the meal (the output).

In this chapter we consider two searching algorithms (sequential search and binary search) and three sorting algorithms (bubblesort, shuttlesort and quicksort).

Searching Algorithms

We wish to examine a list of names (or numbers) to see if it contains a given specific name.

The Sequential Search

In a sequential search, each entry of the list is examined in turn to see if it is the given name. If the name is found its position in the list is noted, otherwise the verdict 'Not in the list' is returned. The algorithm which performs this is:

1   Note the name we wish to find.

2   Starting with the first entry and continuing down the list read each entry to see if it is the given name. If the name is found note the position in the list and stop.

3   If the name is not found note the result 'Name not in list'.

The algorithm could be written in a style more akin to computer programming. The list of names is stored as NAME(1), NAME(2), ... NAME(N).

Input name to be searched; NOM
For I = 1 to N
   If NAME(I) = NOM then print 'Position of NOM is   ', I, and then STOP.
Next I
Print 'NOM is not in the list'
STOP.

The Binary Search

The sequential search algorithm can be applied to any list of names. A more efficient algorithm is the binary search. This can be applied only to a list of names which are in alphabetical order, or a list of numbers which are in increasing order. As in the sequential search the algorithm searches the list for a given name and once found gives the location of the name. If the name is not contained in the list the algorithm concludes with a message to that effect.

The binary search algorithm concentrates on the mid-point of an ever reducing list. To present the algorithm neatly we introduce a tractable notation, and a corresponding convention which allows us to say unambiguously what we mean by 'mid-point'.

For lists with an odd number of names the middle name is obvious. Thus if a list contains 11 names the middle name is the sixth one. Similarly if a list has 17 names the middle one is the ninth name. For lists with an even number of names it is not so clear what ought to be described as 'the middle name'.

Which is the middle name in a list of 6 names?

$$A \quad B \quad C \quad D \quad E \quad F$$

The nearest to a 'middle name' is the third or the fourth. We adopt the convention of choosing the higher numbered item. In the above example we would choose the fourth, D.

It will be useful to adopt the following notation:

$[x]$ = the smallest integer which is greater than or equal to x

Thus for example,

$$[7.3] = 8 \quad [7.9] = 8$$
$$[7] = 7 \quad [6.9] = 7$$

In a list containing N names in alphabetical order, the middle name has position $[(N + 1)/2]$. If N is 20, the middle name has position $[10.5] = 11$. If N is 21 the middle name has position $[11] = 11$. In examining a reducing list of names, say those with positions 15, 16, 17, 18, 19 and 20, then the middle name is at position $[(15 + 20)/2] = [17.5] = 18$.

We wish to search the list for the name NOM. The algorithm compares NOM with the name in position $[(N + 1)/2]$ i.e. the name in the middle of the list. The three possible outcomes of this comparison are:

(1)   NOM is found to be located at this position. The algorithm is now finished.

(2)   NOM occurs before the middle of the list.

(3)   NOM occurs after the middle of the list.

Note that the fact that the list is in alphabetical order allows us to decide which of (2) or (3) actually occurs. If (2) or (3) is the case the algorithm continues in a similar way using a reduced list. For (2) the list is reduced to the names before the middle name; for (3) the list is reduced to all the names after the middle name. In neither case is the middle name included in the new reduced list, as we know this name is not NOM.

The process is now repeated with the reduced list. After each application of the algorithm half of the remaining list is discarded should NOM not be found.

The following example illustrates the binary search algorithm.

EXAMPLE 1

Use the binary search algorithm to locate the names **(i)** GILLANDERS **(ii)** DAVIES in the following list:

1. CONWAY
2. CRANE
3. CURRY
4. DAVISON
5. DOWSON
6. FARMER
7. FOXON
8. GILLANDERS
9. GREGSON
10. HALL
11. HARRISON

Solution

(i) There are 11 names in the list i.e. N = 11.
The middle location is $[(11 + 1)/2] = [6] = 6$ i.e. FARMER.
We know that GILLANDERS must occur in the list *after* FARMER (if at all) and so the list reduces to

7. FOXON
8. GILLANDERS
9. GREGSON
10. HALL
11. HARRISON

At this stage the algorithm has been used once. It is now applied to the reduced list. The middle location is $[(7 + 11)/2] = 9$ i.e. GREGSON. Again, GILLANDERS should occur before GREGSON, so the list becomes simply

7. FOXON
8. GILLANDERS

The algorithm has been used twice. Applying the algorithm again:

The middle location is $[(7 + 8)/2] = 8$ i.e. GILLANDERS.
The name GILLANDERS has been found by the algorithm at position 8. Note that the algorithm has been applied 3 times.

(ii) As in (i) the middle name is at position 6 i.e. FARMER. DAVIES occurs before FARMER so the list is reduced to:

1. CONWAY
2. CRANE
3. CURRY
4. DAVISON
5. DOWSON

The middle location is [(1 + 5)/2] = 3 i.e. CURRY.
DAVIES occurs after CURRY so the list is reduced to

4. DAVISON
5. DOWSON

The middle location is [4.5] = 5 i.e. DOWSON. DAVIES occurs before DOWSON so the list is reduced to

4. DAVISON

Applying the algorithm for a final time results in no list being formed. We can now conclude that DAVIES does not occur in the list.

Sorting Algorithms

We now examine three algorithms which sort lists into order, e.g. alphabetical order, ascending order or descending order. The algorithms are: bubblesort, shuttlesort and quicksort.

Bubblesort

We illustrate the bubblesort algorithm by sorting a list of numbers into ascending order. With each application the bubblesort algorithm succeeds in placing at least one number in its correct position.

We are given a list of N numbers. The algorithm starts at the end of the list and compares the last two numbers, i.e. those in positions N − 1 and N. It places the smaller number first i.e. in position N − 1. This may involve switching the order of the two numbers. The next pair of numbers examined are those in position N − 2 and N − 1. The smaller number is again placed first, i.e. in position N − 2. The next numbers examined are those in position N − 3 and N − 2, and the smaller one is placed in position N − 3. This pattern is repeated. Eventually, the numbers in positions 1 and 2 are examined and the smaller one placed in position 1. At this stage the smallest number in the whole list has successfully been placed in position 1. In this first application of the algorithm (N − 1) pairs of numbers have been examined.

The whole process is now repeated until the numbers in positions 2 and 3 are reached. The smaller of these is placed in position 2, and this means that at this stage the second smallest number has been placed in position 2. Note that in this application of the algorithm, there is no need to involve the number in position 1; we already know it is the smallest. This second application has looked at $(N-2)$ pairs of numbers.

The algorithm is applied repeatedly until no numbers are re-ordered. The numbers in the list are now arranged in ascending order.

We can write this algorithm in a condensed computer program style.

1   Input the list of N numbers
2   Set $K = 1$
3   Set $J = 1$ and $R = 0$
4   Compare the numbers in positions $N - J$, $N - J + 1$ and place the smaller first. Increase R by 1 each time numbers are re-ordered.
5   Increase J by 1 and go to step 4. Do this for each value of J up to and including $J = N - K$.
6   If $R = 0$ go to step 8
    If $R > 0$ go to step 7
7   Increase K by 1 and go to step 3
8   The list is now in ascending order. STOP.

EXAMPLE 2

Use the bubblesort algorithm to arrange the following list of numbers into ascending order.

$$9, \quad 6, \quad 2, \quad 12, \quad 11, \quad 9, \quad 3, \quad 7.$$

Solution

$$9, \quad 6, \quad 2, \quad 12, \quad 11, \quad 9, \quad 3, \quad 7$$

The last pair of numbers are examined and placed in ascending order. In this case there is no change.

$$9, \quad 6, \quad 2, \quad 12, \quad 11, \quad 9, \quad 3, \quad 7$$

The next pair to be examined is 9, 3. They are placed in order producing

$$9, \quad 6, \quad 2, \quad 12, \quad 11, \quad 3, \quad 9, \quad 7$$

The pair 11, 3 is now placed in order giving

$$9, \quad 6, \quad 2, \quad 12, \quad 3, \quad 11, \quad 9, \quad 7$$

Similarly when 12, 3 are placed in order we get

$$9, \quad 6, \quad 2, \quad 3, \quad 12, \quad 11, \quad 9, \quad 7$$

No ordering is needed for the next pair 2, 3

$$9, \quad \boxed{6, \quad 2,} \quad 3, \quad 12, \quad 11, \quad 9, \quad 7$$

The pair 6, 2 is re-ordered.

$$\boxed{9, \quad 2,} \quad 6, \quad 3, \quad 12, \quad 11, \quad 9, \quad 7$$

Finally 9, 2 are re-ordered.

$$2, \quad 9, \quad 6, \quad 3, \quad 12, \quad 11, \quad 9, \quad 7$$

At this stage the smallest number is in its correct position. Seven pairs of numbers have been examined. Note the moving bubble in each of the 7 stages.

Having positioned the '2' correctly, the algorithm is now applied in full to the sub-list

$$9, \quad 6, \quad 3, \quad 12, \quad 11, \quad 9, \quad 7$$

After application of the algorithm the numbers are listed as follows:

$$3, \quad 9, \quad 6, \quad 7, \quad 12, \quad 11, \quad 9$$

Six pairs of numbers have been examined in applying the algorithm to this sub-list. At this stage the '2' and the '3' are correctly positioned, the full list being

$$2, \quad 3, \quad 9, \quad 6, \quad 7, \quad 12, \quad 11, \quad 9$$

The sub-list 9, 6, 7, 12, 11, 9 is now examined. The bubblesort algorithm re-orders these numbers as 6, 9, 7, 9, 12, 11. The sub-list 9, 7, 9, 12, 11 is re-ordered as 7, 9, 9, 11, 12. Application of the algorithm to the sub-list 9, 9, 11, 12 results in no change. The ordering process is complete when no numbers have been interchanged; at this stage all of the numbers are in ascending order. Thus the final ordered list is

$$2, \quad 3, \quad 6, \quad 7, \quad 9, \quad 9, \quad 11, \quad 12.$$

Shuttlesort

This is similar to the bubblesort algorithm in that it arranges a list of numbers into ascending order; pairs of numbers are compared and the smaller placed first.

We are given an unordered list of numbers $a(1)$, $a(2)$, ... $a(N)$. The shuttlesort algorithm 'shuttles' the low numbers to the beginning of the list. The algorithm may be written as follows

1   If $a(1) > a(2)$ then interchange these numbers.
     If $a(1) \leq a(2)$ then leave them.

2   Set $j = 2$

3   Set $i = j$

4   Compare $a(i)$, $a(i + 1)$

5   If $a(i) > a(i + 1)$ interchange these two numbers, decrease i by 1. If $i \geq 1$ go to step 4. If $i = 0$ add 1 to j and go to step 3.
If $a(i) \leq a(i + 1)$ increase j by 1 and go to step 3.

6   Continue until j reaches a value of N, at which time the numbers are in ascending order.

The algorithm is best understood in terms of an example.

EXAMPLE 3

Arrange the following list using the shuttlesort algorithm.

9,   23,   7,   16,   8,   7,   4,   12

Solution

1.   The first pair of numbers (9, 23) is examined and the numbers are interchanged if necessary, the smaller one being placed first. In this example there is no change.

9,   23,   7,   16,   8,   7,   4,   12

2.   The next pair of numbers, (23, 7), is examined i.e. the pair of numbers in positions 2 and 3. The smaller one is placed first. This produces

9,   7,   23,   16,   8,   7,   4,   12

and it is now necessary to go back and examine the first pair (9, 7) again. The list now becomes

7,   9,   23,   16,   8,   7,   4,   12

3.   The numbers in positions 3 and 4 are now compared i.e. (23, 16) and interchanged producing

7,   9,   16,   23,   8,   7,   4,   12

The numbers in positions 2 and 3 are compared i.e.(9, 16). In this example no interchange is necessary and following from previous steps all of the numbers to the beginning of the list are in ascending order.

4.   The numbers in positions 4 and 5 are now examined i.e. (23, 8). Interchanging these produces

7,   9,   16,   8,   23,   7,   4,   12

The numbers in positions 3 and 4 are (16, 8) and these need to be interchanged.

$$7, \quad 9, \quad 8, \quad 16, \quad 23, \quad 7, \quad 4, \quad 12$$

The numbers in positions 2 and 3 are (9, 8) and these are interchanged.

$$7, \quad 8, \quad 9, \quad 16, \quad 23, \quad 7, \quad 4, \quad 12$$

The numbers in positions 1 and 2 are (7, 8) and are obviously left unchanged.

5.   The process is repeated, starting with numbers in positions 5 and 6 i.e. (23, 7). Interchange produces

$$7, \quad 8, \quad 9, \quad 16, \quad 7, \quad 23, \quad 4, \quad 12$$

The numbers in positions 4 and 5 i.e. (16, 7) need to be interchanged.

$$7, \quad 8, \quad 9, \quad 7, \quad 16, \quad 23, \quad 4, \quad 12$$

The numbers in positions 3 and 4 i.e. (9, 7) are interchanged.

$$7, \quad 8, \quad 7, \quad 9, \quad 16, \quad 23, \quad 4, \quad 12$$

The numbers in positions 2 and 3 i.e. (8, 7) are interchanged.

$$7, \quad 7, \quad 8, \quad 9, \quad 16, \quad 23, \quad 4, \quad 12$$

Finally numbers in positions 1 and 2 are examined and no change is necessary.

6.   The numbers in positions 6 and 7 i.e. (23, 4) are compared. After interchanging these the list is

$$7, \quad 7, \quad 8, \quad 9, \quad 16, \quad 4, \quad 23, \quad 12$$

The numbers in positions 5 and 6 i.e. (16, 4) are interchanged.

$$7, \quad 7, \quad 8, \quad 9, \quad 4, \quad 16, \quad 23, \quad 12$$

The numbers in positions 4 and 5, 3 and 4, 2 and 3, 1 and 2 are examined and interchanged when necessary. This finally produces

$$4, \quad 7, \quad 7, \quad 8, \quad 9, \quad 16, \quad 23, \quad 12$$

7.   The pattern is continued. The numbers in positions 7 and 8 i.e. (23, 12) are examined and are interchanged.

$$4, \quad 7, \quad 7, \quad 8, \quad 9, \quad 16, \quad 12, \quad 23$$

The numbers in positions 6 and 7 i.e. (16, 12) are examined and interchanged.

$$4, \quad 7, \quad 7, \quad 8, \quad 9, \quad 12, \quad 16, \quad 23$$

The numbers in positions 5 and 6 i.e. (9, 12) are examined. No interchange is necessary and since all numbers to the left of these are already in ascending order no further interchanges are required. The whole list is now in ascending order.

Quicksort

We mention the quicksort algorithm only briefly. Quicksort is an example of a *recursive* algorithm: an algorithm which calls itself in one of its steps. This algorithm again sorts a list of numbers into ascending order.

EXAMPLE 4

Arrange the list L in ascending order using the quicksort algorithm.

$$L = 16, \quad 21, \quad 15, \quad 3, \quad 12, \quad 9, \quad 17, \quad 27, \quad 6$$

Solution

The quicksort algorithm chooses a specific number from the list, usually that number at the mid-point of the list. In the current example this number is 12. Two lists, L_1 and L_2, are now created. L_1 contains all numbers smaller than 12; L_2 contains all numbers greater than 12. L_1 is formed by reading the original list L from left to right and noting all the numbers smaller than 12 in the order in which they appear. L_2 is similarly formed.

$$3, \quad 9, \quad 6, \quad 12, \quad 16, \quad 21, \quad 15, \quad 17, \quad 27$$

$$L_1 \qquad\qquad L_2$$

In correct position and
so need not be moved.

The algorithm now calls itself, and is applied to the two lists L_1 and L_2. For L_1, the mid-point is 9. All numbers smaller than 9 form list L_3. Since there are no numbers larger than 9 the quicksort algorithm yields

$$3, \quad 6, \quad 9$$

$$L_3$$

For L_2, the mid-point is 15. There are no numbers smaller than 15. All numbers larger than 15 form list L_4.

$$15, \quad 16, \quad 21, \quad 17, \quad 27$$

$$L_4$$

The full list is now

$$3, \quad 6, \quad 9, \quad 12, \quad 15, \quad 16, \quad 21, \quad 17, \quad 27$$

$$\underbrace{}_{L_3} \qquad\qquad \underbrace{}_{L_4}$$

Again the algorithm calls itself and is applied to lists L_3 and L_4. After repeated application the numbers will be in ascending order.

Written in condensed form the quicksort algorithm is:

1   Choose a number from the list; say the number is x.
2   Write all of the numbers smaller than x to the left of x. These numbers form a new list. Write all the numbers larger than x to the right of x. These numbers also form a new list.
3   Apply steps 1 and 2 to each separate list until all of the lists contain only 1 number.
4   The original list is now in ascending order.

Complexity of Algorithms

The complexity of an algorithm is a measure of the computer time needed to implement it. This in turn depends upon the number of operations needed – the total number of additions, subtractions, multiplications, divisions and comparisons for the worst possible case. We need to know how many times loops in the algorithm might be executed.

For example, in the sequential search algorithm we consider the worst possible case, namely when the searched for name does not appear in the list of N names. In this case N comparisons are made before it can be concluded that the name does not appear. The complexity, C, of the algorithm is N.

$$C(\text{sequential search}) = N$$

Let us consider as another example the binary search algorithm applied to a list of N names in alphabetical order. If B(N) is the maximum number of comparisons necessary to locate a given name, then

$$B(N) \le 1 + B\left(\frac{N-1}{2}\right) \text{ if N is odd}$$

$$B(N) \le 1 + B\left(\frac{N}{2}\right) \text{ if N is even}$$

The '1' is the first comparison made, the $B((n-1)/2)$ or $B(n/2)$ term is the number of comparisons needed for the remaining half of the list. (Recall that the binary search algorithm eliminates half of the list with each application.) It can be shown that the above inequality implies the result

$$B(N) \leq 1 + \log_2 N$$

Since

$$1 + \log_2 N \leq N$$

this suggests that the binary search algorithm is more efficient than the sequential search algorithm.

EXAMPLE 5

Show that the complexity (worst case) of the bubblesort algorithm when applied to an unordered list of N numbers is $(N - 1)N/2$.

Solution

Let the complexity be $S(N)$.
After one application of the bubblesort algorithm one number is correctly positioned and $(N - 1)$ may still need to be arranged. This is the worst possible case since there could be more than one number correctly positioned. To place this one number correctly has required $(N - 1)$ comparisons. The complexity of the remaining $N - 1$ unordered numbers is $S(N - 1)$. We can thus state

$$S(N) = S(N - 1) + N - 1$$

This is a *difference equation* and can be solved by standard methods giving

$$S(N) = \frac{(N - 1)N}{2}$$

as required. (Note that difference equations are explained fully in Volume 2.)

One of the weaknesses of defining complexity as above is that it depends upon the *worst* possible case. This worst case may not be very likely to happen in which case the algorithm in practice may be really efficient. More sophisticated definitions of complexity take into account the likelihood of the various cases occurring.

Additional Reading

'Decision Mathematics' The Spode Group, Ellis Horwood, 1986.
'Discrete Mathematics' P.F.Dierker, W.L.Voxman, Harcourt Brace Jovanovich International, 1986.

Exercises

1.1   What are **(i)** the input(s) **(ii)** the outputs of the sequential search algorithm?

1.2   The sequential search algorithm prints the position of the first entry which is NOM and then stops. However a list may contain the name NOM several times. Write an algorithm which outputs the positions of all the NOM entries, or outputs 'NOM not in list' if such is the case.

1.3   A list contains **(i)** 11 **(ii)** 12 names listed alphabetically. What is the maximum number of times the binary search algorithm may have to be applied in locating a given name? Allow for the possibility that the name is not contained in the list.

1.4   A list contains N names listed alphabetically. What is the maximum number of times **(i)** the sequential search algorithm **(ii)** the binary search algorithm may have to be applied before a given name is located?

1.5   A list contains 6 numbers. **(a)** What is the maximum possible number of times the bubblesort algorithm may have to be applied before the numbers are arranged into ascending order? **(b)** What is the maximum number of pairs of numbers that need to be examined?

1.6   A simplified bubblesort algorithm is given by:

1   Input the list of N numbers.
2   Set K = 1.
3   Set J = 1.
4   Look at the numbers in positions N – J, N – J + 1 and place the smaller one first.
5   Increase J by 1 and go to step 4. Do this until J = N – K.
6   Increase K by 1 and go to step 3. Do this until K = N – 1.

Explain the difference between this algorithm and the previous bubblesort algorithm. Which is the more efficient?

1.7   Write an algorithm to find **(a)** the largest **(b)** the smallest number in a given list of N unordered numbers.

1.8   Arrange the following lists of numbers into ascending order using the bubblesort algorithm.

> **(a)** 5 4 3 2 1 0
>
> **(b)** 6 9 –3 4 –17

1.9   Use the shuttlesort algorithm to sort the following lists into ascending order.

> **(a)** 5 4 3 2 1 0
>
> **(b)** 6 9 –3 4 –17

1.10   Arrange the following list into ascending order using the quicksort algorithm.

> 9,   4,   12,   21,   14,   6,   10,   6,   3,   12

See page 111 for solutions.

2

THE TRANSPORTATION PROBLEM

Introduction

Industry is concerned with efficiency at every stage of the research, development and production of an item. Time, man-power, money and materials must be conserved wherever possible. These ideas extend to the distribution of goods from the plants at which they are produced (referred to as *sources*) and to the outlets from which they are sold (referred to as *destinations*). A manufacturer may wish to minimise his distribution costs, or perhaps time is more important and he seeks the speediest distribution plan.

Consider the delivery of goods manufactured at three production plants located in the towns of A, B, C from where they are transported to retail outlets at D, E, F, G.

The plants at A, B, C can produce 15, 35, 20 units respectively. These figures are referred to as the *capacities* of each of the plants.

The retailers at D, E, F, G require 10, 30, 20, 10 items respectively; these figures are referred to as the *demands* at each of the outlets.

At present the manufacturer supplies the goods as shown schematically below:

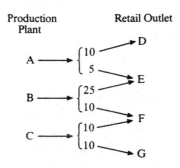

D's allocation of 10 units is supplied by the production plant at A. The demand at E is 30 units, 5 of which are carried from A and the remaining 25 from B, and so on.

Each of the routes along which goods can be carried has associated with it a certain cost. This is usually expressed as the cost to carry each item, which we refer to as the *unit*

17

transportation cost. If the unit transportation cost for the AD route is £5 then the cost of carrying 10 units from A to D is the product of the number of units carried (10) and the unit transportation cost for this route (£5) which is equal to £50.

Having established the plant capacities, the retailers' demands and the unit transportation costs, the manufacturer may begin to question his delivery program. Can he find a cheaper distribution plan?

Although originally concerned with minimising the cost of distribution schedules, the transportation problem has found application in many other areas. One special case is the assignment problem, discussed in Chapter 3, in which personnel are to be allocated to a range of tasks.

The transportation problem also provides a model for deriving production schedules and, for example, by allocating pay-offs to each route it may be used to maximise the profit of a venture.

The solution procedure described below is *iterative*, that is to say an initial solution is derived and updated until no further improvement is possible. It may be necessary to repeat the steps several times and each repetition is called an *iteration*. The initial solution is derived using the following pieces of information:

(1)   the capacity of each plant, or source;

(2)   the demand at each outlet, or destination;

(3)   the unit transportation cost for each route.

This information is usually presented in the form of a table in which each row represents a source and each column a destination.

A Distribution Problem

EXAMPLE 1

Rhyman Simon PLC manufacture Fastercastors, small devices for the easy movement of schoolroom furniture. Goods produced at Addy, Baddy and Caddy are transported to retail outlets at Pest, Quest and Rest. The Government is offering a bonus to those companies which are operating at peak efficiency. With a view to qualifying for this, Rhyman Simon review the distribution of goods between their three production plants and the retailers.

The production capacity of the plants A, B, C are 15, 35, 10 respectively. The retail outlets, P, Q, R, have demands of 10, 30, 20 respectively. The cost of transporting one unit from each plant to each retail outlet is given in Table 2.1.

Table 2.1

| | | Destination | | | Capacity |
		P	Q	R	
	A	4	2	3	15
Source	B	2	4	5	35
	C	3	2	4	10
Demand		10	30	20	

Notice the following points:

Each row of the table corresponds to one of the three production plants and each column represents one of the three retail outlets. The production capacity of the plant at Addy is 15 (Addy can produce 15 cases of the castors each week), while Baddy can make 35. The demand for the product at Pest, for example, is 10 cases per week.

The unit transportation cost for the AP route is 4. That is to say, the cost of carrying one case of castors from Addy to Pest is £4; if 10 cases are transported along this route the total cost would be $10 \times £40 = £40$.

Only the initial letter of each production plant and each retail outlet is used, for convenience.

Using the information given in Table 2.1 the company's Operations Research Officer sets about devising the minimum cost transportation schedule.

The Transportation Algorithm in Three Stages

The method described below involves three procedures which are used in sequence as follows:

Transportation Algorithm

Procedure 1 Find a plan which uses all production and satisfies all demand. This is called the initial solution.

Procedure 2 How much does this solution cost? Can this cost be reduced by transporting some goods along a route which is not used in the current schedule? If yes, identify the route along which the maximum saving is possible and update the plan using Procedure 3. If no, the current solution is optimal; that is to say it is the 'best' (cheapest, or quickest, for example).

Procedure 3 Allocate as many units as possible to the route identified in Procedure 2. Repeat Procedure 2.

Terminate when no further improvement is possible.

Notice the production and demand requirements in Procedure 1. Many real problems do not conform to these constraints but the difficulties are easily overcome by introducing dummy (or fictitious) routes (*see* Example 4).

The Initial Solution: Procedure 1

The initial plan, which is shown in Figure 2.1, is derived using Procedure 1.

Procedure 1

Step 1   Draw a plan with a column for each destination and a row for each source. Each square represents a route between one of the production plants (sources) and one of the retail outlets (destinations). When an allocation has been made to a route the corresponding square is called a non-empty square. Squares corresponding to routes not used in a particular transportation plan are called empty squares. At each step in the development of the initial solution movements are made between the squares, either horizontally or vertically *but never diagonally*! Goto Step 2.

Step 2   Beginning in the top left-hand corner, allocate the maximum available quantity to meet demand at this destination. This is the smaller of (a) the demand at the corresponding destination and (b) the production at this source. Goto Step 3.

Step 3   Is production at this source fully utilised? If yes, goto Step 5. If no, goto Step 4.

Step 4   Move one square to the right and allocate the maximum available quantity which will utilise production without exceeding demand at this destination. Goto Step 3.

Step 5   Move one square down and allocate as many units as possible without exceeding demand at this destination or supply from this source (see Step 2). Repeat Step 3.

Terminate   when all production is utilised and all demand is satisfied.

Returning to the Rhyman Simon problem we follow Procedure 1 to obtain the first solution (Figure 2.1).

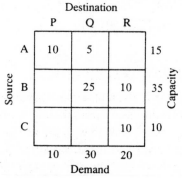

Figure 2.1

Step 1   Shown in Figure 2.1 is a plan with 9 squares, each of which represents a route between one of the three production plants (sources) and one of the three retail outlets (destinations).

Step 2   The demand at P is 10 and the production capacity at A is 15; therefore 10 units are allocated to the AP route.

Step 3   This allocation satisfies the demand at P but there are 5 unused units at A.

Step 4   Move one square to the right and assign these to the AQ route.

Step 3   Production at this source is now fully utilised.

Step 5   There are 35 units available at B and an unfulfilled demand at Q of 25, therefore 25 units are allocated to the BQ route.

Step 3   10 units at B remain unused.

Step 4   These are allocated to the BR route.

Step 3   The production at B is now fully utilised.

Step 5   10 units are required to satisfy demand at R and these are provided by C.

Testing for Optimality: Procedure 2

It may be possible to reduce the cost of the transportation plan by introducing one of those routes not used in the present schedule. Each of the unused routes is considered in turn and the reduction in cost which would be achieved by making an allocation of one unit to each is calculated. This is called the *potential saving* or *shadow cost*. The route with the largest shadow cost is introduced into the schedule and we call this the *entering route* or *entering square*. As one route enters the schedule, another must leave and this is called the *exiting route* or *exiting square*. Sometimes the same saving may be made by introducing one of two or more routes. If this is so it does not matter which is chosen and the tie may be broken arbitrarily (Example 2). There may be a tie for the exiting square, which is also broken arbitrarily (Example 3).

Examination of the Non-empty Squares

First we consider the routes to which an allocation has been made. In order to determine the shadow costs we argue that the cost of transporting one unit along each route currently in use has two components; one associated with the source and one with the destination. The cost to carry one case of Fastercastors from Addy to Quest, for example, is £2. Some of this cost is associated with the production plant at Addy and the remainder is associated with the retailer at Quest. What we do not know at this stage is how the cost is split.

If we let:

$$s_X = \text{cost associated with source X}$$

$$d_Y = \text{cost associated with destination Y}$$

$$t_{XY} = \text{cost of transporting one unit along the XY route}$$

then for each of the routes which are currently being used we can write:

$$t_{XY} = s_X + d_Y \tag{1}$$

The source costs and the destination costs are derived from the non-empty squares using the steps 2, 3, 4, 5 of Procedure 2.

Examination of the Empty Squares

Now we consider the routes which are unused in the current schedule. Once the source and destination costs have been established we use the final step of Procedure 2 to determine the shadow cost of each unused route. This, we argue, is equal to

$$s_X + d_Y - t_{XY} \tag{2}$$

where for each empty square, s, d and t are the corresponding source, destination and unit transportation costs respectively.

It is important to note that (1) is an *equation* which holds for the routes currently in use, while (2) is an *expression* which applies to the unused routes.

We will now state Procedure 2 and illustrate the steps with the Rhyman Simon problem.

Procedure 2

Step 1   The cost of the current schedule is the sum of

unit transportation cost × number of units carried on route

for each of the routes to which an allocation has been made. Goto Step 2.

Step 2   Starting in the top left-hand square, set the cost linked with this source to zero. Goto Step 3.

Step 3   Move along the row to any non-empty squares for which no destination costs have been established. Determine the corresponding destination costs using equation (1). When these are established, or if there are no non-empty squares in this row goto Step 4.

Step 4   Move to the square at the left of the current row, irrespective of its status (empty or non-empty) and move down one square. Goto Step 5.

Step 5   Are there any non-empty squares in this row for which destination costs have been established? If no, goto Step 3. If yes goto the first non-empty square for which a destination cost has been established and calculate the source cost using equation (1). When this has been found goto Step 3.

Step 6   When all source and destination costs are established goto Step 7.

Step 7   Using expression (2) calculate the potential saving associated with each route unused in the present schedule. Identify the largest positive figure.

Terminate   when none of the potential savings found in Step 7 has a positive value.

Returning to the Rhyman Simon problem the solution proceeds as follows.

Step 1   The cost of the initial schedule shown in Figure 2.1 is

$$10 \times £4 + 5 \times £2 + 25 \times £4 + 10 \times £5 + 10 \times £4 = £240$$

Step 2   The source cost s_A is zero.

Step 3   The first non-empty square is AP. The destination cost d_P is calculated from

$$t_{AP} = s_A + d_P$$

$$4 = 0 + d_P$$

$$d_P = 4$$

The next non-empty square is AQ. The destination cost d_Q, calculated in the same way as d_P, is 2. All of the relevant destination costs in this row have now been established.

Step 4   Move back to AP and down to BP.

Step 5   BQ is the first non-empty square in this row for which the destination cost has been found. The source cost s_B is calculated from

$$t_{BQ} = s_B + d_Q$$

$$4 = s_B + 2$$

$$s_B = 2$$

Steps 3, 4, 5 are repeated once more to give the source and destination costs:

$$s_A = 0, \quad s_B = 2, \quad s_C = 1, \quad d_P = 4, \quad d_Q = 2, \quad d_R = 3$$

Step 7   The potential savings associated with those routes currently unused in the initial schedule (Figure 2.1) are

Route	Saving $= s + d - t$
AR	$0 + 3 - 3 = 0$
BP	$2 + 4 - 2 = 4\,^*$
CP	$1 + 4 - 3 = 2$
CQ	$1 + 2 - 2 = 1$

The route which offers the greatest potential saving is BP, marked *, and this becomes the *entering square*.

Improving the Solution: Procedure 3

It is desirable to allocate to the entering route as many units as possible. In this case each item allocated to the BP route will reduce the cost of the present schedule by £4. The maximum adjustment is made while being careful not to exceed the production capacity at the corresponding source (B) or the demand at the corresponding destination (P). Any allocation made to one route therefore necessitates a sequence of adjustments and these are implemented using Procedure 3.

Rules Governing the Re-allocation of Goods

There are two rules which govern the re-allocation of goods:

Rule 1   Within any row or any column there must be only one increasing square (i.e. one route along which more items are to be carried) and one decreasing square (i.e. one route along which fewer items are to be carried).

Rule 2   Adjustments must be made only to non-empty squares, exclusive of the entering square.

These are incorporated into Procedure 3.

Procedure 3

Step 1   In accordance with Rules 1 and 2 determine the sequence of adjustments necessary to balance the schedule when an allocation is made to the entering square. Goto Step 2.

Step 2   Determine the maximum number of units allocated to the entering square. This is equal to the smallest number (of items) in the decreasing squares identified in Step 1.

Step 3   Adjust the current solution to incorporate this change.

Returning to the Rhyman Simon problem the steps necessary to balance the updated schedule are as follows:

Step 1 An allocation to the BP route necessitates a deduction from another route in this row to balance production at B. This is achieved by making an adjustment to the BQ route. A deduction from the BQ route is followed by a positive adjustment to the AQ route to balance demand at Q. Finally, to balance production at A a deduction is made from AP.

The sequence of adjustments is:

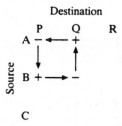

Step 2 The maximum adjustment which can be made at this stage is 10 units; to increase this figure would give rise to a negative quantity in the AP square.

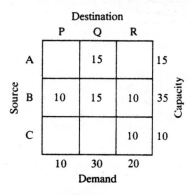

Figure 2.2

We have now completed the first iteration. The updated solution is shown in Figure 2.2. Notice that the AP route is not used in the improved schedule; it is the *exiting square* (or route).

Second Iteration

The cost of the current schedule is:

$$15 \times £2 + 10 \times £2 + 15 \times £4 + 10 \times £5 + 10 \times £4 = £200$$

Notice that the saving made by introducing the BP square is equal to £240 − £200 = £40. This is equal to $10 \times £4$, the number of units along the BP route multiplied by the saving per unit which was calculated in Step 7.

The current solution is tested for optimality using steps 2, 3, 4, 5 of Procedure 2. The source and destination costs are found to be:

$$s_A = 0, \; s_B = 2, \; s_C = 1, \; d_P = 0, \; d_Q = 2, \; d_R = 3$$

The potential savings which could be made by introducing one of the unused routes are:

Route	Saving $= s + d - t$
AP	$0 + 0 - 4 = -4$
AR	$0 + 3 - 3 = 0$
CP	$1 + 0 - 3 = -2$
CQ	$1 + 2 - 2 = 1\,^*$

The only route on which a saving can be made is CQ. For each item allocated to this route a saving of £1 is made. Procedure 3 is repeated to determine how the improvement is to be made. The sequence of adjustments is:

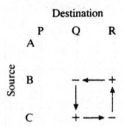

The maximum adjustment which can be made is 10 units.

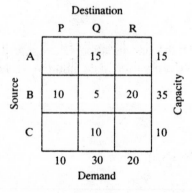

Figure 2.3

We have now completed the second iteration and the updated solution is shown in Figure 2.3. CR is now unused, it is the exiting square.

Third Iteration

The cost of this schedule (Figure 2.3) is

$$15 \times \pounds2 + 10 \times \pounds2 + 5 \times \pounds4 + 20 \times \pounds5 + 10 \times \pounds2 = \pounds190$$

Once again we test for optimality. Steps 2, 3, 4, 6 of Procedure 2 are repeated to determine the source and destination costs:

$$s_A = 0, \; s_B = 2, \; s_C = 0, \; d_P = 0, \; d_Q = 2, \; d_R = 3$$

Repeating Step 7:

Route	Saving $= s + d - t$
AP	$0 + 0 - 4 = -4$
AR	$0 + 3 - 3 = 0$
CP	$0 + 0 - 3 = -3$
CR	$0 + 3 - 4 = -1$ *

and since none of these potential savings is greater than 0, there are no further savings to be made and the schedule shown in Figure 2.3 is optimal.

Summary of Solution

As we have seen, the solution of a transportation problem can be quite lengthy. The iterations can conveniently be summarised as follows.

Initial Solution   Figure 2.1.

First Iteration
Cost of initial solution £240
Source costs for A, B, C are 0, 2, 1 respectively
Destination costs for P, Q, R are 4, 2, 3 respectively.

Route	AR	BP	CP	CQ
Saving	0	4	2	1
Entering square				BP
Adjustment sequence	BP	BQ	AQ	AP
	+	−	+	−
Adjustment quantity				10

Exiting square AP.

Updated solution shown in Figure 2.2.

Second Iteration

Cost of current solution £200.

Source costs for A, B, C are 0, 2, 1 respectively.

Destination costs for P, Q, R are 0, 2, 3 respectively.

Route	AP	AR	CP	CQ
Saving	− 4	0	−2	1
Entering square				CQ
Adjustment sequence	CQ	CR	BR	BQ
	+	−	+	−
Adjustment quantity				10
Exiting square				CR

Updated solution shown in Figure 2.3.

Third Iteration

Cost of current solution £190.

Current solution optimal.

The remaining examples in this chapter will be summarised in this way, in order to focus attention on the essential features of each problem.

A Tie for the Exiting Square

EXAMPLE 2

The changing economic climate has affected the Fastercastor market quite considerably. In the light of several changes which have been made Rhyman Simon again review their distribution schedules.

The information about transportation costs presented in Table 2.1 has been updated, as shown in Table 2.2.

Table 2.2

		Destination			Capacity
		P	Q	R	
	A	12	11	14	13
Source	B	13	13	7	11
	C	10	11	10	12
Demand		10	13	13	36

Previously, the number of non-empty squares (those to which an allocation has been made) in each solution was equal to

number of sources + number of destinations − 1

This is a requirement of the transportation algorithm; the source and destination costs cannot be determined if there are fewer non-empty squares than this number.

At each iteration there is one entering square and one exiting square; the number of non-empty squares does not change. In some problems more than one square becomes empty when the adjustments are made (Step 3, Procedure 3). When this happens, we say that there is a tie for the exiting square. Since only one square can exit at each iteration, one exits as usual and the others are kept in the solution and treated as non-empty squares with allocations of zero. The choice is an arbitrary one and the solution then proceeds as usual.

Summary of Solution

Initial Solution
The initial solution is shown in Figure 2.4.

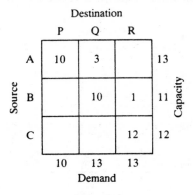

Figure 2.4

First iteration
Cost of initial solution £410.
Source costs for A, B, C are 0, 2, 5 respectively.
Destination costs for P, Q, R are 12, 11, 5 respectively.

Route	AR	BP	CP	CQ
Saving	−9	1	7	5
Entering square				CP

Adjustment sequence is

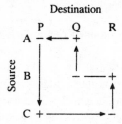

Note that in each row there is only one increasing square and one decreasing square. Similarly in each column there is an increasing square and a decreasing square. All squares used in the sequence, except CP, are non-empty squares.

Adjustment quantity   10

As a consequence of this adjustment, both BQ and AP are empty. The tie is broken arbitrarily; AP is chosen as the exiting square and BQ is treated as a non-empty square with an allocation of zero. BQ is then used in the normal way to determine the source cost s_B and the destination cost d_Q.

The updated solution is shown in Figure 2.5.

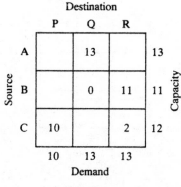

Figure 2.5

Second Iteration
Cost of current solution £340
Source costs for A, B, C are 0, 2, 5 respectively.
Destination costs for P, Q, R are 5, 11, 5 respectively.

Route	AP	AR	BP	CQ
Saving	−7	−9	− 6	5
Entering square				CQ

Adjustment sequence is

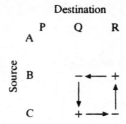

The adjustment quantity is   0
Exiting square   BQ

Updated solution shown in Figure 2.6.

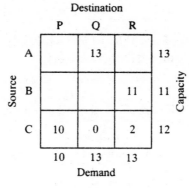

Figure 2.6

Third Iteration
Cost of current schedule £340
The cost of this schedule is exactly the same as that in the second iteration, since all that
has changed is the position of the square which has a zero allocation.
Source costs for A, B, C are 0, −3, 0 respectively.
Destination costs for P, Q, R are 10, 11, 10 respectively.

Route	AP	AR	BP	BQ
Saving	−2	− 4	− 6	−5

There are no further savings to be made, therefore the current solution is optimal.

A Tie for the Entering Square

EXAMPLE 3

Easy Feet have four production plants at which they manufacture a comprehensive range
of casual footwear. Shoes are delivered from these sites to three retail outlets at Achingtoe,
Bunionton and Cornyjoke.

Given in Table 2.3 are the unit transportation costs between the production sites at Eeling, Feltum, Groan and Heely and the three outlets, together with the appropriate production capacities and demand levels.

Table 2.3

		Destination			Capacity
		A	B	C	
	E	8	5	7	30
Source	F	5	5	9	40
	G	7	2	10	50
	H	6	3	15	30
Demand		25	25	100	150

Easy Feet wish to establish a schedule which, while satisfying demands and utilising all production, will minimise their distribution costs.

Initial solution
The initial solution shown in Figure 2.7 is derived using Procedure 1.

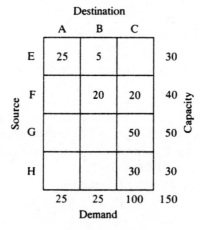

Figure 2.7

First Iteration
The cost of the initial solution is £1455, the source costs for E, F, G, H are 0, 0, 1, 6 respectively and the destination costs for A, B, C are 8, 5, 9 respectively.

The cost of this delivery plan is tested for optimality using Procedure 2 and the potential savings associated with each of the unused routes are:

Route	Saving $= s + d - t$
EC	$0 + 9 - 7 = 2$
FA	$0 + 8 - 5 = 3$
GA	$1 + 8 - 7 = 2$
GB	$1 + 5 - 2 = 4$
HA	$6 + 8 - 6 = 8$ *
HB	$6 + 5 - 3 = 8$ *

1 unit allocated to either HA or HB reduces distribution costs by £8. Either route can be chosen but both cannot be used since one of the requirements of the method we are using is that there is only one entering square. When this happens we say that there is a tie for the entering square. As in Example 2 the tie can be broken arbitrarily and HB is chosen as the entering square.

The solution is completed as in Example 1 and summarised in the usual manner below.

Summary of Solution

Entering square: tie between HA and HB, which is broken arbitrarily. If HB is chosen the solution proceeds as follows.

Adjustment sequence is

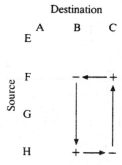

Adjustment quantity		20
Exiting square		FB

Updated solution shown in Figure 2.8

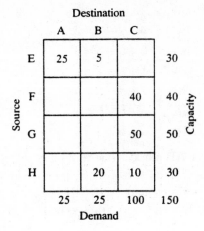

Figure 2.8

Second Iteration
Cost of current solution £1295
Source costs for E, F, G, H are 0, – 8, –7, –2 respectively.
Destination costs for A, B, C are 8, 5, 17 respectively.

Route	EC	FA	FB	GA	GB	HA
Saving	10	–5	– 8	– 6	– 4	0
Entering route						EC

Adjustment sequence is

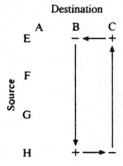

Adjustment quantity	5
Exiting square	EB

Updated solution shown in Figure 2.9.

Destination

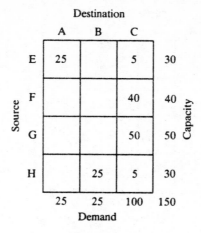

Figure 2.9

Third Iteration

Cost of current solution £1245

Source costs for E, F, G, H are 0, 2, 3, 8 respectively.

Destination costs for A, B, C are 8, –5, 7 respectively.

Route	EB	FA	FB	GA	GB	HA
Saving	–10	5	– 8	4	– 4	10
Entering square						HA

Adjustment sequence is

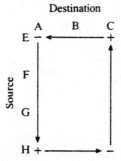

Adjustment quantity	5
Exiting square	HC

Updated solution shown in Figure 2.10.

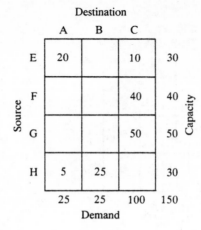

Figure 2.10

Fourth Iteration
Cost of current solution £1195
Source costs for E, F, G, H are respectively 0, 2, 3, –2.
Destination costs for A, B, C are respectively 8, 5, 7.

Route	EB	FA	FB	GA	GB	HC
Saving	0	5	2	4	6	–10
Entering route						GB

Adjustment sequence is

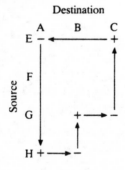

Adjustment quantity	20
Exiting square	EA

The updated solution is shown in Figure 2.11.

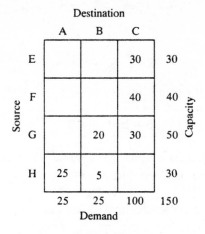

Figure 2.11

Fifth Iteration
Cost of current solution £1075
Source costs for E, F, G, H are 0, 2, 3, 4 respectively.
Destination costs for A, B, C are 2, –1, 7 respectively.

Route	EA	EB	FA	FB	GA	HC
Saving	– 6	– 6	–1	– 4	–2	– 4

Current solution optimal

Dummy Outlets

EXAMPLE 4

Hitemharder produce quality tennis rackets for retail in London, Manchester and Norwich. Given in Table 2.4 are the costs of transporting one racket from each of their three factories which are located in Cardiff, Durham and Edinburgh together with the relevant demands and production capacities.

How are Hitemharder to distribute their products if they wish to minimise the cost of the operation?

Table 2.4

		Destination			Capacity
		L	M	N	
	C	6	10	7	50
Source	D	7	5	8	70
	E	6	7	7	50
Demand		100	30	20	

The total number of rackets produced is the sum of the production capacities at the three plants:

$$50 + 70 + 50 = 170$$

The sum of the demands at the three outlets is:

$$100 + 30 + 20 = 150$$

Hitemharder produce 20 units surplus to demand. They are quite happy with this situation, for the moment, and are interested only in minimising the cost of the distribution schedule.

The transportation algorithm requires that all demands are satisfied and, in addition, that production is fully utilised. Since the last requirement is not met the problem must be moulded until it is. This is achieved simply by inventing a fictitious outlet, O say, to which excess production is directed. This is usually referred to as a *dummy outlet*. The unit transportation costs to this destination are zero.

The solution proceeds as in Example 1 and is summarised in the usual way below.

Summary of Solution

Initial Solution

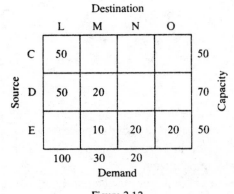

Figure 2.12

Note the introduction of the dummy outlet necessary to equate total production and total demand.
First Iteration
Cost of initial solution £960
Source costs for C, D, E are 0, 1, 3 respectively.
Destination costs for L, M, N, O are 6, 4, 4, -3 respectively.

Route	CM	CN	CO	DN	DO	EL
Saving	− 6	−3	−3	−3	−2	3
Entering square						EL

Adjustment sequence is

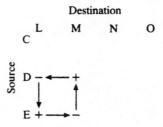

Adjustment quantity	10
Exiting square	EM

Updated solution shown in Figure 2.13

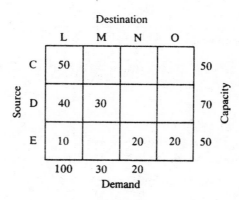

Figure 2.13

Second Iteration
Cost of current solution £930
Source costs for C, D, E are 0, 1, 0 respectively.
Destination costs for L, M, N, O are 6, 4, 7, 0 respectively.

Route	CM	CN	CO	DN	DO	EM
Saving	− 6	0	0	0	1	−3
Entering square						DO

Adjustment sequence is

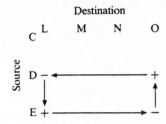

Adjustment quantity   20
Exiting square   EO

Updated solution shown in Figure 2.14

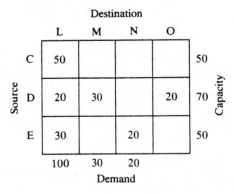

Figure 2.14

Third Iteration
Cost of current solution £910
Source costs for C, D, E are 0, 1, 0 respectively.
Destination costs for L, M, N, O are 6, 4, 7, –1 respectively.

Route	CM	CN	CO	DN	EM	EO
Saving	– 6	0	–1	0	–3	–1

Current solution optimal

Note that the surplus production of 20 units is allocated to the fictitious outlet O.

Exercises

2.1   Trixyclists PLC deliver bicycles from their three plants A, B, C located in Scotland to each of two retail outlets at MaTyresflat and Naybells (M and N respectively). The plant capacities, customer demand and unit transportation costs are given in Table 2.5. Derive the lowest cost transportation schedule.

Table 2.5

		Destination		Capacity
		M	N	
	A	1	7	3
Source	B	8	1	3
	C	9	5	6
Demand		4	8	12

2.2   Devious Danny has two associates Arry (A) and Bertie (B) who supply him with quality Cartyay watches for £1 each. Acting as the middle-man, Danny subsequently sells these watches to friends in Cortcher (C) and Diddlcher (D). This involves some travelling, which Danny doesn't really mind because he sees one or two of his girlfriends while he is on his travels, but he would like to minimise his travelling costs. These costs, with all expenses included, are given in Table 2.6. Also presented are the appropriate supply and demand levels. How is Danny to organise his small business if he is to keep the cost of his journeys as low as possible?

Table 2.6

		Destination		Capacity
		C	D	
	A	9	2	5
Source	B	7	1	7
Demand		4	8	12

2.3   A pharmaceutical company has three factories at Unwell, Verywell and Well (U, V, W). Located at Headache, Eyestrain, Jumpy, and Kold (H, I, J, K) are four dispensaries which must be supplied with the requisite numbers of products. Given the data in Table 2.7 establish the cheapest distribution schedule.

Table 2.7

| | | Destination | | | | Capacity |
		H	I	J	K	
	U	3	6	7	2	5
Source	V	6	4	3	2	12
	W	2	10	7	2	7
Demand		7	8	3	6	24

2.4 A light engineering company manufacture watchermacallits, which are components vital in almost all pieces of machinery. There are three production plants at Anywhere (A), Binthere (B), and Comfromthere (C) and the components are transported to either or both of the industrial towns of Mustgethere (M) and Nevergethere (N). The transportation costs, demands and production capacities are given in Table 2.8. Determine the minimum cost distribution schedule.

Table 2.8

| | | Destination | | Capacity |
		M	N	
	A	2	6	3
Source	B	2	7	5
	C	6	9	2
Demand		6	4	10

2.5 A haulage contractor is making some changes to the running of his small business. Recently profits have dropped and unless he acts quickly the business will collapse. His first step is to gather the following relevant information:

(1) Supply of items at each of the sources from which his lorries collect;
(2) Demand at each of the destinations to which the goods are delivered;
(3) The unit transportation costs (£) for each route;
(4) The time taken (hours) from pick-up to delivery for each route.

Two plans have been suggested to him. Under the first option the minimum cost distribution schedule is determined. In the past, the contractor has given very little thought to running his business efficiently, and minimising his transportation costs seems to him a sensible step to take.

The second option involves contracting out some of the transportation business. Another company in the area has offered to undertake the deliveries and their per-unit transportation costs are directly linked to the time it takes to complete each route as follows:

$$\text{cost } (\pounds) = 0.5 \times \text{time (hours)}$$

Which option should the contractor choose if he is to have the best possible chance of saving his business?

The production capacities, demands and the contractor's own distribution costs are

Table 2.9

		Destination			Capacity
		D	E	F	
	A	2	3	1	8
Source	B	4	4	5	6
	C	2	9	5	5
Demand		5	8	6	19

The times (to the nearest hour) taken to complete the journeys are

Table 2.10

		Destination		
		D	E	F
	A	7	6	9
Source	B	8	8	2
	C	5	6	5

See page 116 for solutions.

3

THE ASSIGNMENT PROBLEM

Introduction

Hair colour, eye colour, height, build and personality are all human characteristics which show a great deal of variation. In much the same way, individuals will perform well in some tasks but badly in others. Management, when presented with a range of jobs to be done and several personnel available to do them, will wish to allocate the tasks in the most efficient way. The aim might be to find the shortest time in which a project can be completed, or we may wish to minimise its cost. These are *minimisation problems* (Examples 1 and 3). The same methods which are used to solve these problems can be applied to *maximisation problems* in which the aim is to maximise the profit of a venture (Example 2).

These problems are special cases of the transportation problem in which the sources are the individuals who carry out the work, and the destinations are the tasks which are to be done. Analogous to the unit transportation costs may be, say, the times taken by each individual to do each of the tasks. Now it is not the quantities shipped along each route which are to be determined (as in the transportation problem) but the particular task which each person is to complete.

Solution of the Assignment Problem

The assignment algorithm is an efficient way of solving the assignment problem. Other techniques do exist but they are not as efficient as the algorithmic approach. Before the assignment algorithm can be applied certain requirements must be met.

Requirements of the Assignment Algorithm

- Each individual must be fully occupied.
- Each task must be completed.
- The number of individuals must equal the number of tasks to be done.

A problem involving n individuals and n tasks is called an 'n by n' problem, written $n \times n$ for convenience.

The algorithm is illustrated by solving several examples.

The Assignment Algorithm

EXAMPLE 1

The Ham family have just finished a splendid Sunday dinner of roast beef and Yorkshire pudding, and everyone begins to clear away the dishes.

Experience has shown that the times each person takes to stack, wash and dry the dishes are those presented in Table 3.1.

Table 3.1

		Task		
		S	W	D
Individual	A	14	12	12
	G	11	8	10
	M	13	16	8

Ann is taking her decision maths examination soon and as a revision exercise she determines the quickest washing up plan.

There are several steps in the solution procedure, and these are summarised below. They are then illustrated in the solution of the Ham family problem.

Assignment Algorithm

Step 1   Subtract the lowest figure in each row from every entry in that row and construct a new table. Total the deductions made. Goto Step 2.

Step 2   Working on the initial table derived in Step 1 subtract the lowest figure in each column from every entry in that column. Construct a new table. Add the total of these subtractions to the previous total of deductions. Goto Step 3.

Step 3   Determine the minimum number of lines which will cover all of the zeros in the table. If, in an $n \times n$ problem, fewer than n lines suffice the solution can be improved, in which case goto Step 4. If at least n lines are needed to cover the zeros the table is optimal, in which case goto Step 5.

Step 4   Locate the smallest number in the latest table which is not covered by the lines drawn in Step 3. Add this figure to the total deductions to date. Subtract it from each uncovered entry. Add it to those figures which are covered twice. Goto Step 3.

Step 5   Assign personnel to the tasks as follows. Locate a row with only one zero in it. The individual in this row is assigned to the task in this column. Cross off the corresponding row and column. This step is repeated until all of the assignments have been made.

Step 6   The time taken to complete all of the tasks is given by the total of the deductions made. This should be equal to the sum of the times for the tasks as performed by the individual concerned in the initial table. When a lot of arithmetic is needed these little checks are necessary.

Returning to the Ham family problem:

Step 1   The lowest figure within each row is subtracted from every entry in that row. These subtractions total 28 (Table 3.2).

Table 3.2

		S	W	Task D	Within row subtractions
	A	14	12	12	12
Individual	G	11	8	10	8
	M	13	16	8	8
Deductions at this stage					28
Total deductions					28

Step 2   The results of the subtractions in Step 1 are given in the body of Table 3.3; that is to say, the nine entries in the three rows A, G, M and the three columns S, W, D.

Table 3.3

		S	Task W	D
	A	2	0	0
Individual	G	3	0	2
	M	5	8	0
Within column subtractions		2	0	0
Deductions at this stage				2
Total deductions				30

The lowest figure within each column is subtracted from every entry in that column. The within column subtractions total 2 (Table 3.3) making a total of $2 + 28 = 30$ subtractions so far.

Step 3   The results of the subtractions in Step 2 are given in the body of Table 3.4.

Table 3.4

		Task		
		S	W	D
	A	0	0	0
Individual	G	1	0	2
	M	3	8	0

Three lines are needed to cover the zeros in Table 3.4 and since this is a 3×3 problem the assignments can be derived from this table.

Step 5   There is a single zero in the M row, D column and another in the G row, W column. Either of these may be chosen first. If we select the zero which lies in the M row, D column, Martin Ham is assigned to drying the dishes. The corresponding row and column are crossed off, giving Table 3.5.

Table 3.5

		Task	
		S	W
Individual	A	0	0
	G	1	0

There is a single zero in the G row. This lies in the W column and therefore Gran Ham is assigned to the washing up.

This leaves Ann Ham to stack the dishes.

Step 6   The total deductions are 30, which means that it will take a total of 30 minutes to complete the tasks. As a check on this arithmetic, this is equal to the sum of the times for each task as performed by the individual concerned given in the original table (Table 3.1) and we may breathe a sigh of relief.

Optimal Assignment

Table 3.6

Task	Individual	Time to complete task
Stack	Ann	14
Wash	Gran	8
Dry	Martin	8

A 3 x 3 Maximisation Problem

EXAMPLE 2

A small group of Japanese ladies gather together to make dolls. The dolls must first be assembled (A), then clothed (C) before they are finally given some hair (H). Being conscious of the competitive business climate the group know that they must strive for efficiency. Which ladies should do which jobs in order to maximise their profit?

Li-Lo (L), Kumengo (K) and See-Sor (S) have determined their hourly profits (in pounds) when each carries out the three tasks (Table 3.7).

Table 3.7

		Task		
		A	C	H
	L	2	3	1
Individual	K	10	11	8
	S	9	5	3

The procedure described in Example 1 provided the solution in a minimisation problem. The technique is very easily adapted to give the solution to a maximisation problem. By minimising the negative of the values given in Table 3.7 the maximum of the profit can be determined. As an illustration of this principle, the maximum of the numbers 1, 2, 3 is 3 and the minimum of the figures −1, −2, −3 is −3. Recall that subtraction of a negative quantity is equivalent to changing the sign and adding.

Reformulation as a Minimisation Problem

The negatives of the data in Table 3.7 are presented in Table 3.8.

Table 3.8

		Task		
		A	C	H
	L	−2	−3	−1
Individual	K	−10	−11	−8
	S	−9	−5	−3

We simply follow the assignment algorithm as in Example 1.

Step 1 The lowest figure in each row is subtracted from every entry in that row (Table 3.9). The total of these deductions is −23.

Table 3.9

		Task			Within row subtractions
		A	C	H	
Individual	L	–2	–3	–1	–3
	K	–10	–11	–8	–11
	S	–9	–5	–3	–9
Deductions at this stage					–23
Total deductions					–23

Step 2 The figures resulting from Step 1 are given in the body of Table 3.10. The lowest figure within each column is next subtracted from every entry in that column (Table 3.10). The total of these deductions is 2, making the total of the subtractions so far $-23 + 2 = -21$.

Table 3.10

		Task		
		A	C	H
Individuals	L	1	0	2
	K	1	0	3
	S	0	4	6
Within column subtractions		0	0	2
Deductions at this stage				2
Total deductions			$-23 + 2 = -21$	

The problem is now straightforward and is completed following the method described in Example 1.

Optimal assignment

Table 3.11

Task	Individual	Hourly profit
Assemble	See-Saw	9
Clothe	Kumengo	11
Hair	Li-Lo	1
Total hourly profit		£21

A 4 x 4 Minimisation Problem

EXAMPLE 3

Vera (V), Wanda (W), Yvonne (Y) and Zara (Z) are employed by a company specialising in the cleaning of executive cars. The interior of each car is hoovered (H), the exterior is polished (P), the engine is checked for oil (E), and the tyres are also checked (T).

Each girl is timed by a time-and-motion expert who has been called in to improve the efficiency of the company. The times taken (in minutes) for each task to be completed are given in Table 3.12.

Table 3.12

		Task			
		H	P	E	T
	V	16	14	13	12
Individual	W	14	17	11	13
	Y	13	14	14	15
	Z	18	16	14	17

There are more calculations to do, but the algorithm is similar in every other respect. The first two steps are shown below.

Step 1 The lowest figure in each row is subtracted from every entry in that row. These within row subtractions total 50 (Table 3.13).

Table 3.13

		Task				Within row subtractions
		H	P	E	T	
	V	16	14	13	12	12
Individual	W	14	17	11	13	11
	Y	13	14	14	15	13
	Z	18	16	14	17	14
Deductions at this stage						50
Total deductions						50

Step 2 The figures resulting from the subtractions in Step 1 are given in the body of Table 3.14.

Table 3.14

| | | Task | | | |
		H	P	E	T
	V	4	2	1	0
Individual	W	3	6	0	2
	Y	0	1	1	2
	Z	4	2	0	3
Within column subtractions		0	1	0	0

The solution then proceeds in the usual manner.

Optimal Assignment

Table 3.15

Task	Individual	Time to complete task
Hoover	Yvonne	13
Polish	Zara	16
Engine	Wanda	11
Tyres	Vera	12
Total time to complete tasks		52 minutes

Exercises

3.1 Dot, Elsie and Fay do some early morning cleaning at the local polytechnic. They split up the chores with some consideration to the total time which they spend working and they wish this to be as small as possible. Any time which is not spent cleaning can be passed much more pleasantly drinking tea in their hideaway!

Which of the tasks hoovering (H), polishing (P) and disposing of the waste (W) should each of the ladies do if the average times (in minutes) spent in each room are

Table 3.16

| | | Task | | |
		H	P	W
	D	2	6	7
Individual	E	8	1	9
	F	6	1	8

3.2 Harry, Ian, John, Kim and Laurie (H, I, J, K, L respectively) work for the local council. Together they paint and decorate council homes as part of the authority's renovation scheme. In all there are 5 tasks involved:

A   any old wallpaper is removed;
B   basecoat is applied to all paintings;
C   walls are cleaned and re-papered after the old paper (if any) has been removed;
D   basecoat on the paintings are sandpapered and dusted ready to be given the final coat;
E   eggshell is applied to all painted surfaces.

The time (in hours) each man takes to complete each task is given in Table 3.17.

In the past the men have found that they can complete a house more quickly if each man does only one part of the operation. The order of the tasks doesn't seem to be too important; because there are always several rooms to be completed one of them is usually ready for a certain job to be done.

How should the tasks be allocated if the overall time to complete a house is to be minimised?

Table 3.17

| | | Task | | | | |
		A	B	C	D	E
Individual	H	2	5	9	1	4
	I	4	2	1	3	9
	J	3	2	5	5	8
	K	4	8	6	4	2
	L	3	9	4	1	7

3.3 Andy, Bill and Charlie (A, B, C respectively) are employed by a large carpet retailer. First the area to be carpeted is measured (M). On delivery the carpet is laid (L) and finally nailed securely to the floor (N) to prevent slipping and stretching.

The times (in minutes) to complete each of the tasks are given in Table 3.18.

Table 3.18

| | | Task | | |
		L	M	N
Individual	A	50	30	60
	B	30	40	50
	C	30	60	40

Allocate the tasks in the most time-efficient way.

3.4   Florrie, Gertie and Hattie (F, G, H respectively) work in the textile industry. There are several steps in the production of knitted garments and each of the ladies has been trained in the three following specific areas:

(1)   Machining of the seams of the garment (M);
(2)   Stoling (S), which is attaching the front and neck-bands of the garments;
(3)   Overlocking (O), which is over-sewing the cut edges to prevent fraying.

   The ladies are paid according to how many garments they can deal with and they obviously wish to work as efficiently as possible. Working as a group the ladies have estimated the numbers of garments (per day) they can process are as follows:

Table 3.19

		Task		
		M	S	O
	F	50	30	60
Individual	G	30	40	50
	H	30	60	40

   If they are to maximise their output how should the ladies choose their tasks?
   Compare the data and solution of this problem with that of Exercise 3.3. What do you notice?

3.5   Resolve Exercise 3.3 using the following presentation:

Table 3.20

		Individual		
		A	B	C
	L	50	30	30
Task	M	30	40	60
	N	60	50	40

   Compare the solution of this question with that of Exercise 3.3. What do you notice?

See page 121 for solutions.

4

LINEAR PROGRAMMING: FORMULATION AND GRAPHICAL SOLUTION

Introduction

Decision making in the real world is usually a complex and very costly affair. Food technologists, for example, must satisfy not only the taste-buds and demand of the consumer but also legislation stipulating, for example, the quantities of additives and lean meat to be included in the recipe. In addition, they must never lose sight of the main objective, which is to make as much profit as possible.

Consider, for example, a firm which produces leather purses and wallets. How many of each should they make if the overall profit is to be maximised? The quantities of each item are called the *decision variables*. If there were unlimited quantities of leather, zippers, man-power and machines the answer to the problem would be simply 'make as many as possible'. But resources are limited and therefore they must be used in the most efficient way.

Fortunately there is a collection of mathematical tools to facilitate the solution of these complex problems. One of the most important is *mathematical programming*. All requirements, restrictions and objectives are expressed as algebraic equations and step-by-step procedures are carried out to give the optimal plan of action (that is, the best plan).

In this text attention is focussed on problems involving linear relationships; that is, those in which the equations relate to straight lines, or planes. More complex tools are needed to deal with non-linear relationships.

Simple problems which involve only two items of manufacture can be solved using graphical techniques. An algebraic method (the simplex algorithm) is used to solve larger problems (Chapter 5).

The first stage in the graphical solution procedure is to formulate the problem as a set of relationships between all of the unknown variables (the decision variables, for example) and the known parameters, such as the profit per item or the quantity of a particular resource available. This is summarised in Procedure 1.

Next a diagram is constructed, each axis on the diagram representing one of the decision variables. The area on the diagram is divided into two regions, the feasible region and the infeasible region. The co-ordinates of points lying in the infeasible region represent solutions which are impossible. They may, for example, indicate that negative numbers of each item are to be produced, or give a production plan which would require more leather than the quantity which is available. Although all points in the feasible region correspond to viable solutions, only one of these is the solution which will maximise the company's profit. This stage is summarised in Procedure 2.

All of the steps in the graphical solution method are summarised and then illustrated in the solution of the first example below.

Formulation of the Linear Program: Procedure 1

EXAMPLE 1 A Maximisation Problem

The Hammer and Nails Furniture Company produces desks and chairs suitable for classroom use. Wood and tubular steel requirements, together with the profit on each item, are given in Table 4.1.

Table 4.1

Item	Wood (m²)	Tubular Steel (m)	Profit per Item (£)
Desk	2	1	5
Chair	1.5	2	4
Quantity Available	30	20	

The production manager wishes to determine how many desks and chairs the company should make in order to maximise profit.

Solution

The Hammer and Nails production planning problem is first formulated as a set of mathematical expressions. The steps of the formulation are summarised in the first procedure.

Procedure 1

Step 1 Define the notation which is to be used throughout the problem. The conventional presentation is described below.

Step 2 Derive the constraints linking the amount of each resource used, in terms of the decision variables, to the quantity available. At this stage some or all of these constraints will be inequalities.

Step 3   Convert any inequalities into equations. This is done by introducing *slack* or *surplus* variables.

Step 4   Formulate the *objective function* in terms of all of the variables introduced in the previous steps.

Let us apply this to the Hammer and Nails furniture problem.

Notation

The letter x, with an appropriate subscript, is used to denote unknowns in the program.

$$\text{Let } x_D = \text{number of desks to be made}$$
$$x_C = \text{number of chairs to be made}$$

x_D and x_C are called *decision variables*, because we have to decide how many desks and how many chairs are to be made.

Constraints

How much of each of the two resources (wood and tubular steel) are consumed if x_D desks and x_C chairs are made?

Using the information given in Table 1.1, (note that we drop the units m² to avoid clutter in the expressions)

$$\text{Wood used in making 1 desk} = 2$$
$$\text{Wood used in making } x_D \text{ desks} = 2x_D$$
$$\text{Wood used in making 1 chair} = 1.5$$
$$\text{Wood used in making } x_C \text{ chairs} = 1.5x_C$$
$$\text{Total wood used} = 2x_D + 1.5x_C$$

Since only 30m² are available

$$2x_D + 1.5x_C \leq 30$$

This inequality is referred to as the wood *constraint*. Note that it is not necessary to use all of the wood. Any remaining is the slack associated with the wood constraint and is denoted by x_W.

Similarly, restrictions on the availibility of the second resource (tubular steel) give rise to another constraint.

$$\text{Tubular steel used in making 1 desk} = 1$$
$$\text{Tubular steel used in making } x_D \text{ desks} = x_D$$
$$\text{Tubular steel used in making 1 chair} = 2$$
$$\text{Tubular steel used in making } x_C \text{ chairs} = 2x_C$$
$$\text{Total tubular steel used} = x_D + 2x_C$$

Since only 20m of tubular steel are available

$$s_D + x_C \leq 20$$

which is the *tubular steel constraint*. The slack associated with this expression is x_T.

It is impossible to make a negative number of desks, or chairs, or to have negative quantities of unused resources so finally we have

$$x_D, \; x_C, \; x_W, \; x_T \geq 0$$

which is the *nonnegativity constraint*.

Objective Function

The aim of this production plan is to maximise profit, P, which may be expressed in terms of the number of desks, x_D, and chairs, x_C produced.

$$\text{Profit on each desk} = 5$$
$$\text{Profit on } x_D \text{ desks} = 5x_D$$
$$\text{Profit on each chair} = 4$$
$$\text{Profit on } x_C \text{ chairs} = 4x_C$$
$$\text{Total profit } P = 5x_D + 4x_C$$

The expression P is called the *objective function*.

Linear Program

The expressions defining the objective function and the wood, tubular steel and non-negativity constraints give the linear program.
Recall that

$$x_D = \text{number of desks to be made}$$
$$x_C = \text{number of chairs to be made}$$
$$x_W = \text{slack associated with the wood constraint}$$
$$x_T = \text{slack associated with tubular steel constraint}$$

Using this notation we can express our problem as follows:

Determine the number of desks and chairs to be made in order to maximise

$$P = 5x_D + 4x_C \qquad \text{(objective function)} \quad (1)$$

subject to the following constraints

$$2x_D + 1.5x_C \le 30 \qquad \text{(wood constraint)} \quad (2)$$
$$x_D + 2x_C \le 20 \qquad \text{(tubular steel constraint)} \quad (3)$$
$$x_D, \; x_C, \; x_W, \; x_T \ge 0 \qquad \text{(non-negativity constraint)} \quad (4)$$

Graphical Solution: Procedure 2

The seven steps in the solution procedure are summarised here for convenience and then illustrated in the text which follows.

Procedure 2

Step 1 Construct one axis for each of the decision variables.

Step 2 Plot one line for each of the constraints.

Step 3 As each constraint is introduced identify the area on the diagram which corresponds to feasible solutions.

Step 4 When all of the lines have been drawn identify the feasible region.

Step 5 Substitute an arbitrary quantity for the left-hand side of the objective function and plot this line on the diagram.

Step 6 Construct a series of lines parallel to the line drawn in the previous step.

Step 7 Locate the corner of the feasible region which corresponds to the optimal solution.

Axes

One axis is drawn to represent x_D, the number of desks to be produced and another for x_C, the number of chairs (Figure 4.1).

Feasible Region

Somewhere on the diagram there lies a point whose coordinates (x_C, x_D) give the optimal solution to the program. Within the feasible region, which is determined by the constraints, all points satisfy the constraint expressions (2), (3), (4). Only one of these points, however, maximises the profit that the company will make and it is this point which gives the desired solution.

All of the points outside of the feasible region give solutions which violate one or more of the constraints, perhaps demanding more wood than the available 30m², or more than 20m of tubular steel. We therefore concentrate on points lying within the feasible region.

How is the feasible region identified? Consider first the wood constraint (2). If x_D and x_C are such that all of the available wood is used, the equation relating wood consumed and wood available is

$$2x_D + 1.5x_C = 30 \qquad\qquad (5)$$

This line divides the diagram into two areas, one containing feasible solutions (so far as the wood constraint alone is concerned) and one which contains infeasible solutions. To distinguish between these two areas it is only necessary to see what happens at one particular, but arbitrarily chosen, point which does not lie in the line itself. The simplest choice is the origin, where $x_D = x_C = 0$. Substituting these values into the left-hand side of equation (5):

$$2(0) + 1.5(0)$$

which is equal to zero. It is certainly true that $0 \le 30$, therefore the origin is a point which satisfies the wood constraint and the area containing this point is feasible. This is indicated on the diagram by shading that side of the line to which the feasible area lies (Figure 4.1).

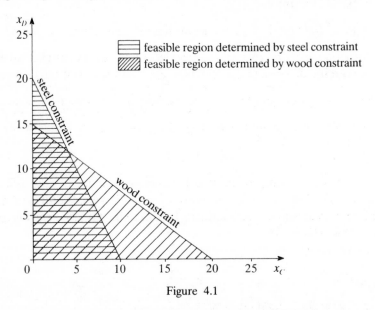

Figure 4.1

The feasible area determined by the tubular steel constraint (3) is identified in the same manner. The entire feasible region is shaded in Figure 4.2.

Where a constraint line passes through the origin (as in Example 2 below), evaluation at the origin is not appropriate and another point must be arbitrarily chosen. However, the principle is the same.

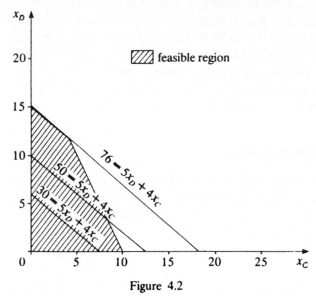

Figure 4.2

Notice that the non-negativity constraint (4) further restricts the feasible region to the upper right quadrant of the diagram.

Profit Line

The objective of the production plan is to maximise the profit, given by equation (1). We need to draw the graph of this equation, but how are we to do this if the left-hand side is unknown?

We begin by choosing an arbitrary value for P, say 30. If we substitute this value into equation (1) we get a new equation, numbered (6).

$$30 = 5x_D + 4x_C \tag{6}$$

Any point on this line lying in the feasible region provides a valid solution with associated profit £30. One such solution is $x_D = 2$, $x_C = 5$. By substituting the profit of each item (Table 4.1) into the right-hand side of equation (6), it is easily seen that the total profit is $5(2) + 4(5) = 30$.

Similarly, points on the line

$$50 = 5x_D + 4x_C \tag{7}$$

give solutions with an associated profit of £50.

The lines which correspond to equations (6) and (7) are parallel, as shown in Figure 4.2. Indeed, no matter what values are assigned to the left-hand side of equation (1), the corresponding lines are parallel. We call these the *iso-profit* lines because 'iso' means 'same', and the lines all have the same slope.

This fact is used to determine the most profitable solution to the linear program. A ruler is placed on one of the iso-profit lines and moved parallel to it, in the direction which improves the value of the objective function. In a maximising case, such as we have here, movement is away from the origin and stops when we reach a point beyond which any further change would yield a solution outside of the feasible region. This point is always at one of the corners of the feasible region, in this example it lies at the intersection of the wood and tubular steel constraint lines (Figure 4.2).

Optimal Solution

The co-ordinates x_C, x_D of the point we have just identified give the optimal solution to the linear program – they tell us how many chairs and desks should be made.

The point of intersection is identified by solving the simultaneous equations corresponding to the wood and tubular steel constraint lines

$$2x_D + 1.5x_C = 30$$
$$x_D + 2x_C = 20$$
$$x_D = 12, \ x_C = 4$$

The optimal solution is to make 12 desks and 4 chairs. The solution quantities $x_D = 12$, $x_C = 4$ are substituted into the objective function (1) to give the profit, P, associated with this plan.

$$P = 5(12) + 4(4)$$
$$P = £76$$

Finally the quantities of unused resources are determined.

$$\text{Wood used} = 2x_D + 1.5x_C$$
$$= 2(12) + 1.5(4)$$
$$= 30$$
$$= \text{wood available}$$

All of the available wood is used and the slack associated with this constraint, x_W, is zero.

$$\text{Tubular steel used} = x_D + 2x_C$$
$$= 12 + 2(4)$$
$$= 20$$
$$= \text{tubular steel available.}$$

All of this resource is used and x_T is zero.

The final solution is

$$x_D = 12 \quad x_C = 4 \quad x_W = x_T = 0 \quad P = £76$$

12 desks and 4 chairs are to be made. This production plan uses all of the available wood and steel and has an associated profit of £76.

Conveniently the number of desks and chairs to be produced are integers but this is not always so. Sometimes the solution quantities turn out to be fractional when clearly a whole number is required. Integer programming techniques overcome this limitation, but are beyond the scope of this text.

A Minimisation Problem

EXAMPLE 2

Mr. Reece-Ole is cooking up a recipe for a new savoury grill containing ham and turkey. He wishes to determine the quantities of the ingredients to be used. His aim is to minimise the cost of production but he must also satisfy three requirements: the total weight of each batch of mix must not exceed 120 kilograms; included must be a minimum of 1.3 kilograms of fat and a minimum of 5 kilograms of protein.

The composition and cost of the ingredients are given in Table 4.2.

Table 4.2

Ingredient (kg)	Fat (kg)	Protein (kg)	Cost (£)
Ham	0.02	0.04	3
Turkey	0.01	0.06	4
Minimum Included	1.3	5.00	

Each kilogram of ham, for example, contains 0.02 kilograms of fat and costs £3, while one kilogram of turkey costs £4 and contains 0.06 kilograms of protein.

Solution – Formulation of the Linear Program

Notation

Let x_H = number of kilograms of ham to be used
x_T = number of kilograms of turkey to be used

Constraints

There are three constraints which must be satisfied. One limits the total weight of the recipe and two further restrictions are concerned with the amounts of fat and protein to be included.

(a) The total weight of the ingredients is $x_H + x_T$ and since this must not exceed 120 kilograms

$$x_H + x_T \leq 120 \qquad \text{(total weight constraint)}$$

(b)

$$\text{Weight of fat in 1 kilogram of ham} = 0.02$$
$$\text{Weight of fat in } x_H \text{ kilogram of ham} = 0.02 x_H$$
$$\text{Weight of fat in 1 kilogram of turkey} = 0.01$$
$$\text{Weight of fat in } x_T \text{ kilogram of ham} = 0.01 x_T$$
$$\text{Weight of fat in mix} = 0.02 x_H + 0.01 x_T$$

Since at least 1.3 kilograms of fat are to be included

$$0.02 x_H + 0.01 x_T \geq 1.3 \qquad \text{(fat constraint)}$$

(c)

$$\text{Weight of protein in 1 kilogram of ham} = 0.04$$
$$\text{Weight of protein in } x_H \text{ kilogram of ham} = 0.04 x_H$$
$$\text{Weight of protein in 1 kilogram of turkey} = 0.06$$
$$\text{Weight of protein in } x_T \text{ kilogram of turkey} = 0.06 x_T$$
$$\text{Weight of protein in the mix} = 0.04 x_H + 0.06 x_T$$

Since at least 5 kilograms of protein are to be included

$$0.04 x_H + 0.06 x_T \geq 5 \qquad \text{(protein constraint)}$$

Objective function

$$\text{Cost of 1 kilogram of ham} = 3$$
$$\text{Cost of } x_H \text{ kilogram of ham} = 3 x_H$$
$$\text{Cost of 1 kilogram of turkey} = 4$$
$$\text{Cost of } x_T \text{ kilogram of turkey} = 4 x_T$$
$$\text{Total cost of mix } C = 3 x_H + 4 x_T$$

Linear program

Let us gather together all of the expressions which comprise the linear program. First we define the notation.

$$x_H = \text{number of kilograms of ham in mix}$$
$$x_T = \text{number of kilograms of turkey in mix}$$
$$x_W = \text{slack associated with the total weight constraint}$$
$$x_F = \text{surplus associated with the fat constraint}$$
$$x_P = \text{surplus associated with the protein constraint}$$

Next we state the objective function, followed by the constraints which apply.

Determine the number of kilograms of ham and turkey Mr. Reece-Ole is to use in producing his new savoury rissoles if he wishes to minimise the cost of the recipe, C, given by

$$C = 3x_H + 4x_T \qquad \text{(objective function)} \quad (8)$$

subject to the following constraints

$$x_H + x_T \le 120 \qquad \text{(weight constraint)} \quad (9)$$
$$0.02x_H + 0.01x_T \ge 1.3 \qquad \text{(fat constraint)} \quad (10)$$
$$0.04x_H + 0.06x_T \ge 5 \qquad \text{(protein constraint)} \quad (11)$$
$$x_H,\ x_T,\ x_W,\ x_F,\ x_P \ge 0 \qquad \text{(non-negativity constraint)} \quad (12)$$

Graphical Solution of the Linear Program

Axes

An axis is drawn to represent each of the decision variables x_H, x_T.

The Feasible Region

First we plot the graph of the equation

$$x_H + s_T = 120 \qquad (13)$$

At the origin ($x_H = x_T = 0$) the left-hand side of equation (13) is zero, satisfying the total weight constraint (9). The origin lies in the feasible area, indicated on the diagram by shading that side of the line (13) to which the origin lies (Figure 4.3).

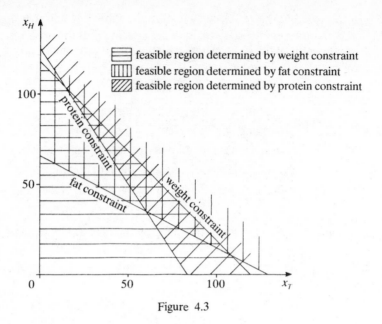

Figure 4.3

Next we plot the graph of the equation

$$0.02x_H + 0.01x_T = 1.3 \tag{14}$$

At the origin, the left-hand side of equation (14) is zero. This violates the fat constraint (10) since at least 1.3 kilograms of fat are required. The origin does not lie in the feasible area, and that side of the line lying away from the origin is shaded (Figure 4.3).

Following the same procedure, the feasible area determined by the protein constraint is identified by plotting the graph of equation (15).

$$0.04x_H + 0.06x_T = 5 \tag{15}$$

Once again, we shade that side of the line we have just drawn which corresponds to feasible solutions (Figure 4.3).

The feasible region for the entire program is the area bounded by the shaded side of each constraint line (Figure 4.4).

The Cost Line

The objective of the linear program is to minimise the cost of the recipe. An arbitrary value is assigned to the left-hand side of equation (8) to give the equation of the first iso-cost line. All cost lines lie parallel to this line, in the same way as the iso-profit lines in Figure 4.2 were parallel to one another. The line which represents the equation

$$240 = 3x_H + 4x_T$$

lies outside of the feasible region. A ruler is placed on this line and moved towards the feasible region. In a minimising problem, movement is towards the origin and stops when the corner of the feasible area nearest to the origin is reached.

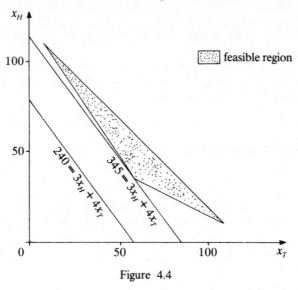

Figure 4.4

Optimal Solution

The optimal solution is at the intersection of the fat and protein constraint lines which correspond to equations (14) and (15). Solving the equations simultaneously gives the solution values of the decision variables.

$$0.02x_H + 0.01x_T = 1.3$$
$$0.04x_H + 0.06x_T = 5$$

$$x_H = 35, \ x_T = 60$$

The optimal recipe therefore contains 35 kilograms of ham and 60 kilograms of turkey. The cost of this mixture is

$$C = 3(35) + 4(60)$$
$$C = £345$$

The total weight of the ingredients, $x_H + x_T$, is $35 + 60 = 95$ kilograms. Since up to 120 kilograms of meat could have been included the slack x_W associated with this constraint is $120 - 95 = 25$ kilograms.

  'Less-than' inequalities have associated slack. Any 'spare' associated with a > constraint is referred to as surplus. The fat content is found by substituting the solution values (60, 35) into equation (10). This gives

$$0.02(35) + 0.01(60) = 1.3 \text{ kilograms}$$

which is the minimum required. There is no surplus, x_F, associated with this constraint.
The protein constraint (11) is also satisfied exactly and x_P is zero.
The final solution is

$$x_H = 35 \quad x_T = 60 \quad x_W = 25 \quad x_F = x_P = 0 \quad C = £345$$

Mr. Reece-Ole should include 35 kilograms of ham and 60 kilograms of turkey in his recipe. This mixture will weigh 95 kilograms and will cost £345. Included will be 1.3 kilograms of fat and 5 kilograms of protein.

An Investment Problem

EXAMPLE 3

Al MacApacket, a succesful Scots entrepreneur, has £10,000 to be invested in two bonds A and B. A yields 10% per annum, B yields 8%. Al believes that variety is the spice of life and accordingly decides to invest no more than £8,000 in either option.
How much should Al invest in each bond in order to maximise his yield?

Solution – Formulation of the Linear Program

Notation

$$\text{Let } x_A = \text{sum to be invested in A}$$
$$x_B = \text{sum to be invested in B}$$

Constraints

Total amount to be invested $= x_A + x_B$
Al wishes to invest all of his capital, therefore

$$x_A + x_B = 10,000 \qquad \text{(total investment constraint)}$$

No more than £8,000 is to be invested in either A or B and so we have the two constraints

$$x_A \leq 8,000 \qquad \text{(constraint for maximum investment in A)}$$
$$x_B \leq 8,000 \qquad \text{(constraint for maximum investment in B)}$$

Objective Function

$$\text{Yield on £1 invested in A} = 0.10$$

Yield on x_A invested in A $= 0.10x_A$
Yield on £1 invested in B $= 0.08$
Yield on x_B invested in B $= 0.08x_B$
Total yield $Y = 0.10x_A + 0.08x_B$

Linear Program

The notation we are using is

x_A = sum to be invested in A
x_B = sum to be invested in B

x_{MA} = slack associated with constraint for maximum investment in A
x_{MB} = slack associated with constraint for maximum investment in B

Now we state the objective of the exercise, followed by the constraints which apply.
  Determine the amount of money Al should invest in each of the two bonds A and B if he is to maximise his yield, Y, given by

$$Y = 0.10x_A + 0.08x_B \qquad \text{(objective function)} \quad (16)$$

subject to

$$x_A + x_B = 10{,}000 \qquad \text{(total investment constraint)} \quad (17)$$
$$x_A \le 8{,}000 \qquad \text{(maximum investment in A)} \quad (18)$$
$$x_B \le 8{,}000 \qquad \text{(maximum investment in B)} \quad (19)$$
$$x_A,\ x_B,\ x_{MA},\ x_{MB} \ge 0 \qquad \text{(non-negativity constraint)} \quad (20)$$

Graphical Solution of the Linear Program

Axes

An axis is drawn to represent each of the decision variables x_A and x_B.

Feasible Region

The total investment constraint is given by equation (17). The graph of this equation is a straight line and since Al wishes to invest all of his capital, the feasible area corresponding to this constraint is the line itself (Figure 4.5). Points which do not lie on this line do not satisfy the total investment constraint which is given by equation (17).
  The constraint for the maximum investment in A is given by the inequality (18). First we plot the graph of equation (21).

$$x_A = 8{,}000 \qquad (21)$$

This is a straight line, shown in Figure 4.5. At the origin, the left-hand side of equation (21) is zero, satisfying the constraint (18). Therefore the origin lies in the feasible area determined by this constraint and this is indicated by shading the appropriate side of the line (Figure 4.5). The feasible area determined by the constraint (19) is found in the same manner (Figure 4.5).

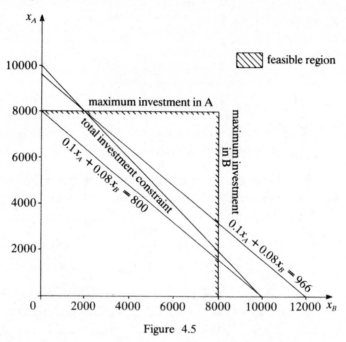

Figure 4.5

The feasible region is the section of the total investment line satisfying constraints (18), (19).

Yield line

The objective of the linear program is to maximise Al's yield. Assigning an arbitrary value of £800 to the left-hand side of equation (16) gives

$$0.1x_A + 0.08x_B = 800$$

The graph of this equation is shown in Figure 4.5. A ruler is placed on this line and moved towards the feasible region. Movement stops when the point on the feasible region which is furthest from the origin is reached.

As we move a ruler towards the segment of the line which defines our feasible region we find that the first feasible point is $x_A = 2,000$, $x_B = 8,000$. The associated yield is found by substituting into equation (16)

$$0.10(2,000) + 0.08(8,000) = £840$$

If we move our ruler further away from the origin we find that the optimal values of the decision variables x_A, x_B are the co-ordinates of the point of intersection of the line corresponding to equation (17) and the graph of the equation $x_A = 8,000$. This gives $x_A = 8,000$, $x_B = 2,000$. Substituting these figures into the objective function defined by equation (16) gives a yield of $Y = £960$.

The constraint defined by equation (18) is satisfied exactly and the slack associated with it, x_{MA}, is zero.

The slack associated with constraint defined by equation (19), x_{MB}, is

$$8,000 - 2,000 = 6,000$$

The final solution is

$$x_A = £8,000 \quad x_B = £2,000 \quad x_{MA} = £0 \quad x_{MB} = £6,000 \quad Y = £960$$

£8,000 are to be invested in A and £2, 000 in B. The yield on these investments will be £960.

Exercises

4.1   Determine the slack or surplus associated with each set of constraints and solutions:

(i) $x_1 = 2$ $x_2 = 3$

(a) $x_1 + x_2 \leq 5$	(b) $2x_1 + 4x_2 \leq 17$
(c) $x_1 + 3x_2 \geq 10$	(d) $x_2 \geq 3$

(ii) $x_1 = 100$ $x_2 = 50$

(a) $0.1x_1 - 0.2x_2 \geq 0$	(b) $x_1 + 3x_2 \leq 500$

(c) $10x_1 + 30x_2 \leq 3500$

(iii) $x_1 = 92$ $x_2 = 41$

(a) $x_1 + x_2 \leq 150$	(b) $x_1 \geq 50$
(c) $x_2 \leq 50$	(d) $x_1 - x_2 \geq 0$

4.2   Plot the feasible region determined by each of the following sets of constraints:

(i) $x_1 + 2x_2 \geq 4$
    $2x_1 + x_2 \leq 6$
        $x_1, x_2 \geq 0$

(ii) $x_1 + x_2 \leq 10$

$0.3x_1 + x_2 \geq 2.1$

$x_2 \leq 6$

$x_1, x_2 \geq 0$

(iii) $x_1 + x_2 = 100$

$x_2 \geq 20$

$x_1, x_2 \geq 0$

4.3   Determine the optimal solution for x_1, x_2 and the corresponding value of the objective function in each of the following:

(i)   maximise $P = x_1 + x_2$

subject to $x_1 + 4x_2 \geq 10$

$x_1 \geq 2$

$5x_1 + 4x_2 \leq 40$

$x_1, x_2 \geq 0$

(ii)   maximise $P = x_1 + 2x_2$

subject to $x_1 + x_2 \leq 200$

$2x_1 + x_2 \geq 200$

$3x_1 - x_2 \leq 300$

(iii)   minimise $C = 2x_1 + x_2$

subject to $x_2 \geq 4$

$x_1 \geq 4$

$x_1 + x_2 \geq 10$

(iv)   minimise $C = 2x_1 + x_2$

subject to $3x_1 - x_2 \leq 400$

$x_2 - x_1 \leq 200$

$3x_1 + x_2 \geq 600$

4.4 Solve the following using the graphical method:

(i) Buttons and Bows produce two versions of a dress: 'Modern Miss', which is for retail in the High Street, and 'Young Designer', which is to be sold exclusively in the company's New Bond Street boutique.

The following data apply:

Item	Sewing Time (hours)	Fabric Required (m)	Profit (£)
Modern Miss	1	3	15
Young Designer	2	3	40
Resource Available	40	90	

How many of each garment should Buttons and Bows make if they are to maximise their profit?

(ii) Crooked Cuthbert has £80 to invest in a new business venture. After many hours of deliberation, he buys himself a second-hand suitcase to serve as his new mobile sales premises. This costs him £5. He then sets out to visit a friend in the wholesale business.

Pete the Poser has a new consignment of Channel Number 6 perfume and genuine high-class Spade vases. Providing that Cuthbert takes at least 20 bottles of perfume, at the bargain price of 75p a bottle, Pete asks only £1 each for the vases.

Cuthbert estimates that he will make 20p profit on each bottle of perfume, and 30p profit on each of the vases. He decides to go ahead with the purchase of these items and if there is any money left after his purchase he will celebrate his investment with a jar or two at his local.

There is only one further consideration, which is the total weight of his stock. Pete warns Cuthbert that it may be necessary for him to beat a hasty retreat, should the long arm of the law appear. The weight of each bottle of perfume is 0.2 kilograms; vases weigh 0.4 kilograms each and Cuthbert reckons he could carry his case plus 20 kilograms of stock, and still run quickly, should the need arise!

How many of each item should Cuthbert buy in order to maximise his profit?

See page 125 for solutions.

5

LINEAR PROGRAMMING: SIMPLEX METHOD

Introduction

The Hammer and Nails Furniture company specialise in the manufacture of classroom furniture. Their initial range was limited to the production of desks and chairs and an optimal plan was derived in Chapter 4 using the graphical method. The firm now wishes to introduce black-board stands to their range of classroom furniture. There are three decision variables:

$$x_D = \text{number of desks to be made}$$
$$x_C = \text{number of chairs to be made}$$
$$x_S = \text{number of stands to be made}$$

The graphical solution of the extended problem involves three-dimensional geometry, which is rather complicated and not practical. If there are more than three decision variables in the problem, the graphical method breaks down completely.

An alternative solution procedure is the *simplex algorithm* which can be used to solve any linear program. Basically there are four stages. First the linear program must be prepared in a form suitable for the simplex method. An initial solution is found and examined to determine whether or not it can be improved. If an improvement is possible, changes are made according to certain rules, and a new solution is derived. This process is repeated until no further improvements can be made.

We will now resolve Hammer and Nails' original problem (Chapter 4) using the simplex algorithm in order to illustrate the principles on which the method is based and how it is used. The techniques are easily extended to include extra decision variables.

Formulation of the Linear Program

The original linear program was:

maximise $\qquad\qquad\qquad P = 5x_D + 4x_C \qquad\qquad$ (objective function)

subject to the following constraints:

$$2x_D + 1.5x_C \leq 30 \qquad \text{(wood constraint)}$$
$$x_D + 2x_C \leq 20 \qquad \text{(tubular steel constraint)}$$
$$x_D, x_C, x_W, x_T \geq 0 \qquad \text{(non-negativity constraint)}$$

where x_W and x_T are slack variables (Chapter 4). The simplex method requires that all the constraint inequalities, with the exception of the non-negativity constraints, should be replaced by corresponding equalities. Further, *all* variables must be incorporated into *each* equation. Let us take the wood constraint:

$$2x_D + 1.5x_C \leq 30$$

to illustrate how these requirements are fulfilled. Whatever the values of x_D, x_C in the optimal production plan the amount of wood used ($2x_D + 1.5x_C$) and the amount unused (x_W, the slack) must total 30m². Therefore,

$$2x_D + 1.5x_C + x_W = 30 \qquad (1)$$

This equation now meets the first requirement of the simplex algorithm. Similarly, the equation derived from the steel constraint by introducing the slack variable x_T is

$$x_D + 2x_C + x_T = 20 \qquad (2)$$

There is still a little more work to be done in order to satisfy the second of the simplex requirements, which is that all variables must appear in each equation. Without changing the validity of equation (1) we can write

$$2x_D + 1.5x_C + 1x_W + 0x_T = 30 \qquad (3)$$

Whatever the value of x_T, when multiplied by 0 it makes no contribution to the left-hand side of equation (3). Similarly, x_W is introduced into equation (2) to give

$$x_D + 2x_C + 0x_W + 1x_T = 20 \qquad (4)$$

Notice that x_W in equation (1) and x_T in equation (2) have been written (equivalently) $1x_W$ and $1x_T$ in equations (3) and (4) respectively. This is purely for convenience in a subsequent stage of the solution and does not affect the validity of the equations.

The objective function must also be written as an equation in which all of the variables appear. We rewrite the equation for the objective function P as

$$P = 5x_D + 4x_C + 0x_W + 0x_T \qquad (5)$$

The coefficients of the slack variables x_W and x_T in equation (5) are zero. This reflects the fact that while each desk, for example, contributes £5 profit, there is no gain on left-over resources (which is what x_W, x_T represent).

Rewriting the program in a form suitable for simplex, the notation is first defined:

$$x_D = \text{number of desks to be made}$$

x_C = number of chairs to be made

x_W = slack associated with the wood constraint

x_T = slack associated with the tubular steel constraint

and the linear program is stated:

Determine the number of desks and chairs which should be made if the company are to maximimise the profit, P, given by:

$$P = 5x_D + 4x_C + 0x_W + 0x_T \qquad \text{(objective function)} \quad (6)$$

subject to the following constraints:

$$2x_D + 1.5x_C + 1x_W + 0x_T = 30 \qquad \text{(wood constraint)} \quad (7)$$

$$x_D + 2x_C + 0x_W + 1x_T = 20 \qquad \text{(tubular steel constraint)} \quad (8)$$

$$x_D, x_C, x_W, x_T \geq 0 \qquad \text{(non-negativity constraint)} \quad (9)$$

Optimal Solution as a Corner of the Feasible Region

The values of x_D and x_C in the optimal production plan are found by solving equations (7) and (8). There are four unknowns: x_D, x_C, x_W and x_T but only two equations. In general, solutions to any set of simultaneous equations with more unknowns than equations can be found only by assigning arbitrary values to some of those unknowns. As an aid to readers who are unfamiliar with this procedure an example is given at the end of this chapter in Appendix 1 (*see* p. 86).

In order to solve equations (7) and (8) arbitrary values must be assigned to two of the four variables x_D, x_C, x_W and x_T. Which two should we choose and what values should we give to them? We will now systematically take pairs of the variables, arbitrarily assign to them the value zero, and solve the equations which follow. This generates four (of many) solutions to equations (7) and (8) and these are given in Table 5.1.

Table 5.1

$x_D = x_C = 0$	$x_W = 30$	$x_T = 20$
$x_C = x_W = 0$	$x_T = 5$	$x_D = 15$
$x_W = x_T = 0$	$x_D = 12$	$x_C = 4$
$x_T = x_D = 0$	$x_C = 10$	$x_W = 15$

The feasible region of the original linear program was constructed in Chapter 4. It is reproduced here for convenience (Figure 5.1).

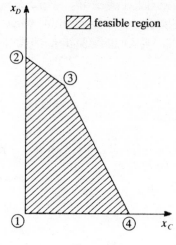

Figure 5.1

In fact, each of the solutions in Table 5.1 corresponds to one of the corners of the feasible region in Figure 5.1. Given in Table 5.2 are the values of each of the variables x_D, x_C, x_W, x_T at these corners and the corresponding profits P, found by substituting into the right-hand side of equation (6).

Table 5.2

corner point	solution value at corner point				profit (£)
	x_D	x_C	x_W	x_T	P
1	0	0	30	20	0
2	15	0	0	5	75
3	12	4	0	0	76
4	0	10	15	0	40

In general, it can be shown that each corner of the feasible region of any linear program corresponds to a solution of that program. Moreover, one of these corners corresponds to the optimal solution we are trying to find.

Based on the information in Table 5.2, Hammer and Nails's optimal strategy is to make 12 desks and 4 chairs, giving a profit of £76. This is in agreement with the solution obtained using the graphical method.

Although the solution to this linear program can be simply determined by examining the four corner points of the feasible region, enumeration of all corner points in a real problem would be a very lengthy task indeed. The simplex algorithm is a procedure in which only a few carefully selected corner points are examined, beginning with the origin. Each time a new corner is considered, the corresponding value of the objective function (in this case the amount of profit made, P) is improved.

The initial table, or *tableau* as it is more usually known, is constructed using

Procedure 1. The solution can be extracted from this, or any other tableau in the solution, using Procedure 2. Procedure 3 is then used to determine whether or not improvements can be made. We usually call this part of the method *testing for optimality*. When no further improvement is possible we say that the current solution is *optimal*.

Initial Tableau: Procedure 1

The initial tableau is constructed using Procedure 1, which may be illustrated best by looking at the finished table and making some simple observations.

Tableau 1

basic variables	x_D	x_C	x_W	x_T	solution quantity b	row number
x_W	2	1.5	1	0	30	(i)
x_T	1	2	0	1	20	(ii)
P	5	4	0	0	0	(iii)

Column Headings

Each of the seven columns has a title. We will skip the first column and come back to it shortly. There is one column for each variable in the problem (columns 2, 3, 4, 5) and these are headed by the symbols we are using to denote them (x_D, x_C, x_W, x_T). The values in column 6 are the solution quantities of the variable named in column 1. For example, the value of x_W in Tableau 1 is 30. We can now come back to column 1, which is headed *basic variables*. Any variable named in this column is said to be *in the basis* and has the value shown in the solution quantity column. A *non-basic variable* does not appear in this column and has the value zero. In this tableau, x_W (slack wood) and x_T (slack tubular steel) are in the basis and are equal to 30 and 20 respectively. As x_D and x_C are non-basic variables they are equal to zero. Finally, since the entries in the rows of the tableau change as the solution proceeds, we label each with a number in the final column.

Rows

In addition to the headings, there are three rows in the initial tableau; one corresponding to each resource constraint in the problem and one for the objective function. Row 1 corresponds to the wood constraint and we have denoted this by writing x_W in the first column. Compare the entries in this row with equation (7). Row 2 corresponds to the steel constraint and, finally, row 3 corresponds to the objective function.

We will now state Procedure 1, which was used to derive Tableau 1. The reader will find it of benefit to work through this with close reference to Tableau 1 and the linear program as stated in equations (6), (7), (8) and (9).

Procedure 1

Step 1   Construct a table in which the number of columns is equal to the number of variables (the objective function is not included) plus 3, and the number of rows is equal to the number of constraints (excluding the non-negativity constraint) plus 1.

Step 2   Give titles to the columns. Column 1 is headed 'basic variables'. In the following columns enter the names of the variables in the program (not including the objective function). The final two columns are headed 'solution quantity' (usually symbolised by the letter b) and 'row number' respectively.

Step 3   In column 1, row 1 write the symbolic name of the slack variable corresponding to the first constraint (x_W in this case). In the following columns, enter the coefficients of the variables in this constraint as it was stated in the reformulated linear program, including the right-hand side of the equation. Number this row 1. Repeat this for each constraint, numbering the rows appropriately.

Step 4   Write the symbolic name of the objective function (P in this example) in the first column. The coefficient of each of the variables in the objective function is entered in the appropriate column. The entry in the solution quantity column is zero.

Interpretation of the Tableau: Procedure 2

Procedure 2 applies to all tableaux constructed in the course of the solution of a linear program, as will be illustrated below for each of the three tableaux we derive.

Procedure 2

Step 1   The value of each variable listed at the left-hand side of the tableau (i.e. the value of each variable in the basis), is the value given in the *solution quantity* column.

Step 2   All variables not in the basis are equal to zero.

Step 3   The value of the objective function is the negative of the solution quantity in the final row of the tableau.

Interpretation of the first tableau is almost always trivial: it is usually 'produce nothing'. Working with reference to Tableau 1, x_D and x_C are the non-basic variables. Each is equal to 0 which means that no desks and no chairs are to be produced. x_W, x_T are the basic variables. Their values are 30 and 20 respectively and this tells us that 30m² of wood and 20m of tubular steel remain unused. The value of the objective function, that is the profit associated with this production plan, is £0.

Testing for Optimality: Procedure 3

Procedure 3 is used to test successive solutions for optimality. We determine which of the non-basic variables (which are set to zero in the current solution) is to have a non-zero value in the next solution. The criterion adopted is that the variable coming into the basis is the one which gives the greatest improvement of the objective function. We identify it as that variable which has the largest positive value in the objective function row. A new tableau is then constructed using row operations given in Procedure 3 below. (*See also* Appendix 2, p. 87.)

We will now state this procedure and illustrate it with the Hammer and Nails problem. In some of these steps division has been denoted by /, for convenience of presentation.

Procedure 3

Step 1 Locate the largest positive value in the objective function row. The corresponding column is the *pivot column* and the corresponding variable is the *entering variable*.

Step 2 For each row (excluding the objective function row) calculate the ratio

$$\text{solution quantity} \,/\, \text{coefficient in pivot column}$$

conventionally written b/c.

Step 3 Select the smallest of the ratios calculated in Step 2, ignoring any negative values. The variable listed at the left-hand side of this row is the *exiting variable*. The figure in the pivot column of this row is the *pivot element*.

Step 4 Replace the name of the exiting variable listed at the left-hand side of the tableau by the name of the entering variable. This row now corresponds to the entering variable.

Step 5 Continue working on the same row as in Step 4 and use row operations as in Step 6 until the pivot element is equal to 1.

Step 6 The new coefficient in each column of the current row is equal to

$$\text{old coefficient} \,/\, \text{pivot element}$$

An alternative presentation of this calculation and one which fits neatly into the tableau, is

$$\text{old coefficient} \times (1/\text{pivot element})$$

Step 7   Work on all remaining rows, including the objective function row, and use row operations as in Step 8 below to obtain a coefficient of 0 in the current pivot column.

Step 8   Within each row note the figure in the pivot column. Multiply this by –1. Take this figure and multiply the new coefficients determined in Step 6 by it. Add these coefficients to those in this old row. There will now be a zero in the pivot column of the newly generated row.

Step 9   When there are no positive values in the objective function row the current solution is optimal and can be extracted using Procedure 2.

Following Procedure 3, the solution of the Hammer and Nails problem proceeds as follows.

Step 1   We see by inspection of Tableau 1 that the largest coefficient in the profit row is 5. The *entering variable*, that is the variable coming into the basis, is x_D. The column of coefficients

$$2$$
$$1$$
$$5$$

is the *pivot column*.

Step 2   The ratios

$$\frac{\text{solution quantity}}{\text{coefficient of variable in pivot column}}$$

for the x_W, x_T rows are 15 (30/2) and 20 (20/1), respectively.

Step 3   The smaller of the ratios is 15, which is in the x_W row, and therefore x_W is the exiting variable. (*See* Appendix 3, p. 89.)

Step 4   We draw up a new tableau in which the name of the exiting variable, x_W, at the left-hand side of row (i) is replaced by the name of the entering variable, x_D.

Step 5   We continue working on the coefficients in this row, which are:

$$2 \ \ 3/2 \ \ 1 \ \ 0 \ \ 30$$

The pivot element is equal to 2 and we are required to make this figure equal to 1.

Step 6   The new coefficient in each column of the current row is therefore

$$\text{old coefficient} / 2$$

This gives row (iv) shown in Tableau 2.

Steps 7, 8   Working now on the x_T row, the figure in the pivot column is 1, which we multiply by –1 to give –1. The coefficients in row (iv) (Tableau 2) are multiplied by this figure, giving

$$-1 \ -3/4 \ -1/2 \ 0 \ -15$$

These are added to the coefficients in the old x_T row (row (ii), Tableau 1) to give

$$0 \ 5/4 \ -1/2 \ 1 \ 5$$

This is the new x_T row, numbered (v). Notice that negative entries in the table are acceptable. These calculations are repeated to give the new objective function row (vi).

All of the calculations we have done are summarised in Tableau 2, immediately before the 'basic variables' column.

Tableau 2

	basic variables	x_D	x_C	x_W	x_T	solution quantity b	row no.	ratio b/c
row (i)/2	x_D	1	3/4	1/2	0	15	(iv)	$15/(3/4) = 20$
row (ii) + (−1.row(iv))	x_T	0	5/4	−1/2	1	5	(v)	$5/(5/4) = 4$
row (iii) + (−5.row(iv))	P	0	1/4	−5/2	0	−75	(vi)	

We use Procedure 2 to extract the solution

$$x_D = 15 \ \ x_C = 0 \ \ x_W = 0 \ \ x_T = 5 \ \ P = £75$$

A Further Iteration

The largest *positive* quantity in the objective function row of Tableau 2 is $1/4$, therefore x_C is the entering variable. The smallest positive ratio b/c is 4, therefore the exiting variable is x_T.

Tableau 3

	basic variables	x_D	x_C	x_W	x_T	solution quantity b	row number
row (iv) + (−3/4.row (viii))	x_D	1	0	4/5	−3/5	12	(vii)
row (v) × 4/5	x_C	0	1	−2/5	4/5	4	(viii)
row (vi) + (−1/4.row(viii))	P	0	0	−12/5	−1/5	−76	(ix)

The solution, extracted using Procedure 3, is

$$x_D = 12 \ \ x_C = 4 \ \ x_W = 0 \ \ x_T = 0 \ \ P = \pounds 76$$

and since there are no positive values in the objective function row this solution is optimal.

Exercises

5.1   Find the solution values for x and y when **(a)** $z = 0$, **(b)** $z = 1$, **(c)** $z = 2$:

(i)
$$2x + 3y + 2z = 8$$
$$3x + y + z = 5$$

(ii)
$$x - y + z = 10$$
$$2x + y - 2z = 5$$

(iii)
$$-3x + 2y + z = 7$$
$$2x + 3z = -2$$

5.2   Find the solution values for p and q when **(i)** $r = s = 0$, **(ii)** $r = s = 1$, **(iii)** $r = s = 2$:

$$4p - q + r + 2s = 11$$
$$p + 2q + s = 5$$

5.3   Resolve Exercise 4.4(i) using the simplex method. Compare the profit in every tableau with that at one of the corners of the feasible region in the graphical solution of the problems.

5.4   The linear programs we have solved using the simplex method have each involved the maximisation of an objective function subject to several 'less than or equal to' inequalities. The linear program in Exercise 4.4(i), which includes the constraint $X_P \geq 20$, can also be solved using simplex but requires a little more preparation before the first tableau is constructed.

'Less than or equal to' inequalities, such as the cost constraint in the Crooked Cuthbert program

$$0.75X_P + X_V \leq 75 \tag{1}$$

are converted to equalities by incorporating a slack variable. Thus (1) may be written

$$0.75X_P + X_V + X_C = 75 \qquad (2)$$

where X_C is a slack variable. Applying the same principle to the demand constraint ($X_P \geq 20$) and incorporating a slack variable, X_D, gives

$$X_P - X_D = 20 \qquad (3)$$

The simplex algorithm works by setting a number of variables equal to zero at each iteration. Initially X_P and X_V, the decision variables, are zero. Substituting $X_P = 0$ into (3) gives

$$-X_D = 20$$
$$\text{i.e. } X_D = -20$$

But this is in conflict with the non-negativity constraint, which states that all variables must be greater than or equal to zero.

We overcome this difficulty by introducing an artificial variable. Incorporating this into the demand constraint gives

$$X_P - X_D + a_D = 20 \qquad (4)$$

Initially, X_P and X_D are kept in the basis and are equal to zero. Therefore in the first solution a_D is equal to 20.

We exclude the artificial variable from the final solution by giving it a large negative profit, $-m$.

The first tableau for the Crooked Cuthbert problem is given below. Obtain the final solution.

Tableau 1

basic variables	X_P	X_V	X_D	a_D	X_C	X_W	solution quantity b	row	ratio (b/c)
a_D	1	0	−1	1	0	0	20	1	
X_C	3/4	1	0	0	1	0	75	2	75
X_W	1/5	2/5	0	0	0	1	20	3	50
P	1/5	3/10	0	0	0	0	0	4	

5.5   In an effort to shed some weight (and the nick-name it attracts!) Cuddles restricts her calorific intake. Her diet allows a Saturday treat of 1,000 calories. In order of preference, Cuddles likes cheesecake, milk chocolate and toffee. Although cheesecake is her favourite goodie, it doesn't last very long and Cuddles would like her treat to last for at least 30 minutes.

Using the following information, determine how much of each of the foods should make up the treat if Cuddles is to maximise her units of pleasure.

Treat	Time to eat (mins)	Calories per 100 grams	Units of pleasure
Cheesecake	10	300	8
Milk chocolate	20	600	7
Toffee	90	500	4

See page 130 for solutions.

Appendix 1

Solution of Systems of Linear Equations with more Unknowns than Equations

$$x + 2y = 7$$

is an equation with two unknowns x and y. If x is given an arbitrary value of 3, for example, we have

$$3 + 2y = 7$$
$$y = 2$$

Thus, $x = 3, y = 2$ is one of many solutions of the equation. Another solution is $x = 1, y = 3$. The value of y in each solution depends upon the value given to x.

This principle applies to larger systems of equations. For example

$$2x + 4y + 3z = 17 \tag{A1}$$
$$x + y + z = 6 \tag{A2}$$

is a system of two equations involving three unknowns and may be solved by choosing an arbitrary value for x, y or z.

If we let $z = 3$, and substitute this value into equations (A1) and (A2), we have

$$2x + 4y + 3(3) = 17$$
$$x + y + 3 = 6$$

so that

$$2x + 4y = 8 \tag{A3}$$
$$x + y = 3 \tag{A4}$$

Solving equations (A3) and (A4) for x and y gives $x = 2, y = 1$. Therefore, $x = 2, y = 1$, $z = 3$ is one of the many possible solutions to the original system of equations.

Appendix 2

Solution of Constraint Equations Using Row Operations

The procedure may be summarised in four steps, and these will be illustrated using a straightforward example. Although this particular example is trivial, the method described applies to much more complex systems of equations.

Solve

$$3x - y + z = 1$$
$$2x + 4y - 2z = 10$$

First we write the equations in the form

x	y	z	solution quantity	row number
3	−1	1	1	(A5)
2	4	−2	10	(A6)

We work with respect to the first variable, x, as follows:

(a) multiply row (A5) by the reciprocal of the coefficient of x in row (A5) to give row (A7),

(b) multiply row (A7) by $(-1 \times$ coefficient of x in row (A6)) and add the result to row (A6) to give row (A8).

	x	y	z	solution quantity	row number
row(A5) × (1/3)	1	−1/3	1/3	1/3	(A7)
row(A6) + (row(A7) × (−2))	0	14/3	−8/3	28/3	(A8)

Now we repeat step 2, working with respect to the next variable, in this case y:

(a) multiply row (A8) by the reciprocal of the coefficient of y in row (A8) to give row (A10),

(b) multiply row (A10) by $(-1 \times$ coefficient of y in row(A7)) and add the result to row (A7) to give row (A9).

	x	y	z	solution quantity	row number
row(A7) + (row(A10) × (1/3)	1	0	1/7	1	(A9)
row(A8) × (3/14))	0	1	−8/14	2	(A10)

Finally, we set z to the value for which the particular solution is required and read off the solution quantities for x and y. As we have seen in the linear programming problem, we let some of the variables be equal to zero. Accordingly we will let z be equal to zero in this example.

$$\text{Substituting } z = 0 \text{ in row (A9) gives } x + (1/7)(0) = 1$$
$$x = 1$$
$$\text{Substituting } z = 0 \text{ in row (A10) gives } y − (8/14)(0) = 2$$
$$y = 2$$

Similar analysis can be applied to a system of equations with 4 variables.

$$3w−x+y+2z = 1$$
$$2w + 4x − 2y − z = 10$$
$$w−x + 3y + 7z = 20$$

First we write the equations in the form:

w	x	y	z	solution quantity	row number
3	−1	1	2	1	(A11)
2	4	−2	−1	10	(A12)
1	−1	3	7	20	(A13)

Working with the first variable, w:

(a) multiply row (A11) by 1/3 to give row (A14).

(b) multiply row (A14) by −2 and add to row (A12). This produces row (A15).

(c) multiply row (A14) by −1 and add to row (A13) to produce row (A16).

w	x	y	z	solution quantity	row number
1	−1/3	1/3	2/3	1/3	(A14)
0	14/3	−8/3	−7/3	28/3	(A15)
1	−2/3	8/3	19/3	59/3	(A16)

We now work with the next variable, x:

(a) multiply row (A15) by 3/14 to give row (A18).

(b) multiply row (A18) by 1/3 and add to row (A14) to produce row (A17).

(c) multiply row (A18) by 2/3 and add to row (A16) to produce row (A19).

w	x	y	z	solution quantity	row number
1	0	1/7	1/2	1	(A17)
0	1	– 4/7	–1/2	2	(A18)
0	0	16/7	6	21	(A19)

Finally we work with y:

(a) multiply row (A19) by 7/16 to produce row (A22).

(b) multiply row (A22) by 4/7 and add to row (A18). This produces row (A21).

(c) multiply row (A22) by –1/7 and add to row (A17) to produce row (A20).

w	x	y	z	solution quantity	row number
1	0	0	1/8	–5/16	(A20)
0	1	0	1	29/4	(A21)
0	0	1	21/8	147/16	(A22)

If $z = 0$ then $w = -5/16$, $x = 29/4$ and $y = 147/16$.

Appendix 3

Choice of Variable to Exit the Basis

Which of the basic variables x_W, x_T is to be replaced by x_D?

Rows (i) and (ii) of Tableau 1 in the text can be written

$$2x_D + 1.5x_C + x_W = 30$$
$$x_D + 2x_C + x_T = 20$$

$$x_W = 30 - 2x_D - 1.5x_C \tag{A23}$$
$$x_T = 20 - x_D - 2x_C \tag{A24}$$

By how much can the new basic variable, x_D, be increased before the left-hand side of each equation becomes less than zero, thereby violating the non-negativity constraint?

Setting $x_C = 0$ for the moment, we see from equation (A23) that an increase of 1 in x_D decreases x_W by 2 i.e the coefficient of x_D in the wood constraint. x_D can be increased up to $30/2 = 15$ before x_W becomes zero or less.

Similarly, in equation (A24), x_D can be increased by a figure of up to $20/1 = 20$ before x_T becomes zero or less.

x_W is chosen as the exiting variable since it reaches zero first.

For row (i) of Tableau 1 in the text the ratio b/c is $30/2 = 15$.
For row (ii) of Tableau 1 in the text the ratio b/c is $20/1 = 20$.

The smallest positive ratio is 15, so the exiting variable is x_W.

6

TWO-PERSON ZERO-SUM GAMES

Introduction

The decision-making problems described in Chapters 4 and 5 involved one agent who, when faced with several alternatives, chooses the strategy which will optimise the value of his objective function. He may, for example, wish to maximise his profit or minimise his costs.

Games theory provides a method for analysing decisions which are made interactively i.e. between two or more agents. Food manufacturers, for example, must consider not only their own costs and profit margins but also the prices of similar items marketed by their competitors. In drawing up programme schedules television companies give a great deal of consideration to the alternatives offered by their rivals. When making a decision each agent or *player* must evaluate the consequences of his action on his own objective function (his gain or loss, for example) and on his opponent's subsequent behaviour. Although the competitors have no way of knowing their opponent's response they may have a jolly good guess!

The analysis of small games is reasonably straightforward and some simple examples are described below (Examples 1 to 5). More complex situations are analysed by formulating the problem as a linear program as in Example 6. This is solved using the simplex method, but the details are beyond the scope of this book.

In the games described in Examples 1 and 2, each player has complete information about the pay-offs both receive under each of the options. The players select the action which maximises their gain, or equivalently (as will be demonstrated), minimises their loss. This is called their *optimal strategy*. Having identified the best course of action each player will not change his strategy; to do so would involve either a smaller gain or a bigger loss. We say that each player adopts a *pure strategy*.

In some games it is impossible to identify a pure strategy and a strategy which incorporates the elements of chance is adopted. We call this a *mixed strategy*. The derivation of this strategy is described in Example 3.

The problem can sometimes be simplified by eliminating one or more of the choices each player can make, as in Examples 4 and 5. These are actions which are identfiable as less favourable to one of the players.

Maximin Pay-off Strategy for a 2 x 2 Game with a Saddle Point

EXAMPLE 1

Bill and Ben while away the boring mathematics lesson by playing pen-and-ruler. This is a simple game in which either may choose a pen or a ruler. Money is exchanged according to the joint outcomes. The sums involved (in pence) are shown in Table 6.1.

Table 6.1

		Ben	
		Pen	Ruler
Bill	Pen	5	10
	Ruler	4	6

The game is fatuous from Ben's point of view since he is always going to lose. However the example does serve to illustrate some points of game theory. Table 6.1 shows the conventional presentation of games theory information. The entries in the table, the *pay-offs*, are the sums that are given to the player whose options are listed at the left-hand side of the table. In this game Bill receives from Ben the amounts of money shown in Table 6.1. If, for example, both players choose a pen, Ben gives 5p to Bill; if Bill chooses a pen and Ben a ruler, Bill receives 10p from Ben, and so on. Although money may not always be involved the outcome must be quantified in this way.

The game which Bill and Ben are playing is a *two-person zero-sum game*. The first part of the name is obvious, the second part may not be. The entries in the table are the sums of money Ben gives to Bill. Ben's loss is Bill's gain. If both players choose a ruler Bill receives 6p from Ben; Bill's gain is + 6p, Ben's loss is – 6p and the two figures sum to zero.

As in all decision-making problems the rules and the objective, or aim, of the game must be clearly stated at the outset. In the models described below each player's objective is to maximise his gain, or equivalently, to minimise his loss. This equivalence is demonstrated below. The strategy is often referred to as the *minimax loss strategy* or the *maximin pay-off strategy*. The basic philosophy is 'choose the best of the worst'. The player asks 'what is the worst outcome if I choose each of the strategies open to me?'. The action which has associated with it the least damaging of these 'worst' outcomes is selected.

In this very simple game we see that Bill is bound to gain and Ben to lose. Therefore Bill's objective is obviously to win as much as possible while Ben's is to minimise his (inevitable) loss.

Maximin Pay-off Strategy

Each row of Table 6.1 represents one of Bill's choices. The first step in the analysis of the game is to determine Bill's smallest pay-off for each choice. These sums are shown in Table 6.2. The minimum pay-off when Bill chooses a pen is 5p and should he select a ruler his smallest pay-off is 4p.

Table 6.2

		Ben		Bill's minimum pay-off
		Pen	Ruler	
Bill	Pen	5	10	5
	Ruler	4	6	4
Ben's maximum loss		5	10	

Bill, wishing to make as much money as he can, chooses the action which guarantees the highest minimum gain. This minimum gain is 5p should he select a pen and 4p if he chooses a ruler. Bill's maximin pay-off strategy is to choose the act which maximises his minimum pay-off. The 'best of the worst' is 5p, and Bill selects a pen.

Minimax Loss Strategy

Since Bill's gain is Ben's loss, the strategy of each player may be determined from the same table. Viewing the game from Ben's position, each column represents one of his choices. The greatest loss he suffers for each of his choices is shown in Table 6.2. When Ben selects a pen his largest loss is 5p, and the greatest loss should he select a ruler is 10p. Not wishing to risk a possible loss of 10p he chooses a pen. The minimax loss strategy is that which minimises a player's maximum potential loss.

Equivalence of Maximin Pay-off and Minimax Loss Strategies

Now we will view the game in terms of Ben's pay-off and derive his maximin pay-off strategy. As we will demonstrate, this is equivalent to Ben's minimax loss strategy.

Table 6.3

		Bill		Ben's minimum pay-off
		Pen	Ruler	
Ben	Pen	−5	− 4	−5
	Ruler	−10	− 6	−10
Bill's maximum loss		−5	− 4	

Given in Table 6.3 are Ben's pay-offs, presented in the conventional way. The entries are the sums of money Ben receives from Bill. The negative values indicate that Ben is actually losing this amount to Bill and since every entry in the table is negative Ben is always the loser.

If Ben chooses a pen his minimum pay-off is –5p i.e. he must give Bill 5p. Should Ben select a ruler his minimum pay-off is –10p. The best of the worst, Ben's maximin pay-off strategy, is the action which maximises his minimum pay-off. Therefore, Ben should choose a pen and this selection is in agreement with that previously derived as his minimax loss strategy.

The calculations involved in the determination of Bill's minimax loss strategy are also shown in Table 6.3. If Bill chooses a pen the worst outcome is when Ben also chooses a pen; the pay-off is –5p which represents a gain of 5p (to Bill). Had Ben chosen a ruler, Bill's loss would have been –10p i.e. Bill would have received 10p from Ben. Hence the worst outcome should Bill choose a pen is that he will gain 5p. Similarly the worst outcome when Bill chooses a ruler is when Ben chooses a pen; the pay-off is then – 4p representing a payment to Bill from Ben of 4p. The minimum of Bill's maximum potential losses is –5p (–5p is less than – 4p) and the strategy Bill adopts is to choose a pen.

Saddle Point of the Game

Bill's maximin pay-off strategy is to choose a pen, guaranteeing a payment to him of at least 5p. Ben's minimax loss strategy is to choose a pen too, limiting his loss to 5p. This figure is the *saddle-point* of the game. Notice that it is the smallest figure in its row and the largest figure in its column (Table 6.2).

Value of the Game

The *value* of the game is the pay-off in the saddle point position, which is 5p (to Bill).

Equilibrium Act Pair

The acts which correspond to the saddle point of the game are the *equilibrium act pair*. In this example 'Bill chooses a pen, Ben chooses a pen' are the equilibrium act pair.

Optimal Strategies

Bill's optimal strategy is to choose a pen.
Ben's optimal strategy is to choose a pen.
Value of the game is 5p (to Bill).

Maximin Pay-off Strategy for a 3 x 2 Game with a Saddle Point

EXAMPLE 2

Ben expresses some disillusionment with the game, realising that he is always the loser. Bill suggests that they expand the game by giving Ben a third choice of a calculator. The pay-offs to Bill in this game are given in Table 6.4. Is this game more profitable to Ben than the original version?

Table 6.4

		Pen	Ben Ruler	Calculator	Bill's minimum pay-off
Bill	Pen	4	6	− 4	− 4
	Ruler	3	7	− 1	− 1
Ben's maximum loss		4	7	− 1	

Bill's Maximin Pay-off Strategy

Should Bill select a pen the worst that he can do is to receive a pay-off of − 4p i.e. he loses 4p to Ben. The minimum pay-off when he chooses a ruler is –1p; that is to say, he makes a payment to Ben of 1p. The best of the worst outcomes, the maximum of Bill's minimum pay-offs is –1p, when he chooses a ruler.

Ben's Minimax Loss Strategy

In choosing a pen Ben risks a maximum loss of 4p. Should he select a ruler he may lose 7p. Ben's maximum loss if he chooses a calculator is –1p. As this is expressed in terms of Bill's pay-off, Ben actually gains 1p from Bill. Therefore, Ben's minimax loss strategy is to pick a calculator, when he gains 1p from Bill.

Saddle Point of the Game

The smallest figure in row 1 of Table 6.4 is − 4. It is not the largest value in its column and is therefore not the saddle point of the game.

The smallest figure in row 2 of Table 6.4 is –1 and, since it is also the largest figure in its column, it is the saddle point of the game.

Value of the Game

The value of the game is –1p (to Bill). This is more favourable to Ben than the previous version which has a value of 5p (to Bill).

Equilibrium Act Pair

The equilibrium act pair, the pair of actions associated with the saddle point position, is a choice of ruler by Bill and a choice of calculator by Ben.

Optimal Strategies

Bill's optimal strategy is to choose a ruler.
Ben's optimal strategy is to choose a calculator.
The value of the game is −1p (to Bill).

Mixed Strategies for a 2 x 2 Game with no Saddle Point

EXAMPLE 3

At this point Ben's interest wanes and he quits the game. Big Bertha, who sits in front of Bill, has a large bag of toffees and suggests that she and Bill play for sweeties. Bill digs deep into his desk and produces some rather dusty chocolate eclairs and play begins. In the game each player chooses a colour, either pink or white, and the following pay-offs apply.

Table 6.5

		Bertha	
		Pink	White
Bill	Pink	3	4
	White	9	−3

The saddle point of a game, defined as the smallest figure in its column and the largest in its row, gives the players' maximin pay-off strategies. This game has no saddle point and an alternative to the maximin pay-off analysis is needed.

The strategies previously detailed involved an equilibrium act pair. Having determined the choice which optimises his objective, each player would not deviate from that selection. This is a pure strategy in which only one act is chosen, time after time . . . .

A game without a saddle point has no equilibrium act pair and the players adopt a *mixed strategy* in which any one of several acts may be chosen in the course of the game. The choice could be made in a totally random way but there is a superior alternative. Each player makes his selection according to the rules of probability in such a way that he maximises his gain in the long run, irrespective of the choice made by his opponent. Some of the time a player will choose one act, some of the time he will choose another and what we have to determine are the probabilities with which he makes those choices. (*See* Appendix 1, p. 108.)

The strategy for each player is considered separately and we begin with Bill.

Formulation of Expected Pay-off Equations

Let p be equal to the probability that Bill chooses pink and $1-p$ the probability with which he chooses white. We must establish the value of p.

We said that each player wishes to maximise his gain 'in the long run'. We quantify this as the player's *expected pay-off* (*see* Appendix 2). Bill's expected pay-off is defined as:

$$(\text{probability of outcome}_1 \times \text{pay--off associated with outcome}_1)$$

$$+$$

$$(\text{probability of outcome}_2 \times \text{pay--off associated with outcome}_2)$$

where outcome$_1$ is 'Bill chooses pink' and outcome$_2$ is 'Bill chooses white'.

Using the information in Table 6.5 we find one expression for Bill's expected gain, in terms of p, when Bertha chooses pink and another when she chooses white.

When Bertha selects pink, Bill's expected gain $= 3p + 9(1 - p)$

$$= -6p + 9 \qquad (1)$$

When Bertha selects white, Bill's expected gain $= 4p - 3(1 - p)$

$$= 7p - 3 \qquad (2)$$

Solution of Expected Pay-off Equations

Since p is a probability it takes values in the interval $(0, 1)$. Shown in Figure 6.1 are the graphs of $-6p + 9$ and $7p - 3$ as p varies over this interval.

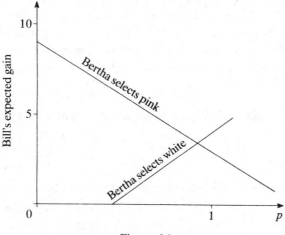

Figure 6.1

These lines correspond to Bill's expected gain under each of Bertha's strategies and they intersect at the point $p = 12/13$. This value may be read directly from Figure 6.1 or more accurately determined algebraically as the solution of

$$-6p + 9 = 7p - 3$$
$$p = 12/13$$

Look closely at Figure 6.1. If Bill chooses a value of p less than 12/13 his expected pay-off will be much higher when Bertha selects pink rather than white. Guessing this, Bertha would select white to limit Bill's expected gain. If Bill chooses a value of p greater than 12/13, his expected pay-off will be higher if Bertha selects white rather than pink. Guessing this, Bertha would choose pink to limit Bill's gain. Bill wishes to maximise his expected gain whatever choice Bertha makes and this he can do by adopting a mixed strategy in which he chooses pink with probability $p = 12/13$ and white with probability 1/13.

Value of the Game

The value of the game is Bill's expected pay-off. This is determined from the graph or by substituting $p = 12/13$ into the right-hand side of either equation (1) or equation (2).

value of the game = 45/13 (to Bill).

We will now find Bertha's mixed strategy

Formulation of Expected Pay-off Equations

Let q be equal to the probability that Bertha chooses pink and $1 - q$ the probability that she chooses white. We must determine the value of q which will minimise her loss, irrespective of Bill's choice. The argument is similar to that used to determine the equations for Bill's expected pay-off. However, we must remember that the information in Table 6.5 relates to Bill's pay-off and therefore measures Bertha's loss which we now wish to minimise.

When Bill selects pink his expected gain = Bertha's expected loss
$$= 3q + 4(1 - q)$$
$$= -q + 4 \qquad (3)$$

When Bill selects white his expected gain = Bertha's expected loss
$$= 9q - 3(1 - q)$$
$$= 12q - 3 \qquad (4)$$

The lines corresponding to equations (3) and (4) are plotted, for values of q ranging from

0 to 1 (Figure 6.2). These intersect at the point where $q = 7/13$. This can be read directly from the graph, or established algebraically as the solution of

$$-q + 4 = 12q - 3$$
$$q = 7/13$$

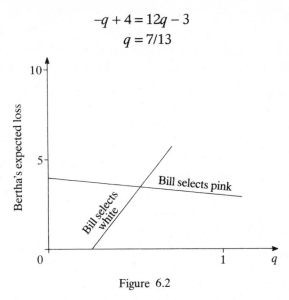

Figure 6.2

If Bertha selects a value of q less than 7/13, Bill's expected gain, equivalently Bertha's expected loss, will be greater when he chooses pink rather than white. If Bertha selects a value of q greater than 7/13, she would lose more when Bill chose white than when he chose pink. Wishing to minimise her loss irrespective of Bill's choice, Bertha plays the game with a mixed strategy in which she chooses pink with probability $q = 7/13$ and white with probability 6/13.

Value of the Game

In agreement with the figure derived earlier, the value of the game which is found by substituting $q = 7/13$ into the right-hand side of either equation (3) or equation (4) is 45/13 (to Bill).

Optimal Strategies

Bill's optimal mixed strategy is to choose pink with probability 12/13 and white with probability 1/13. That is to say Bill should choose pink (on average) 12 times out of a run of 13 games, and white only once.

Bertha's optimal mixed strategy is to choose pink with probability 7/13 and white with probability 6/13. On average Bertha chooses pink 7 times out of every 13 games, and white 6 times out of every 13 games.

The value of the game is 45/13 (to Bill).

Elimination of Inadmissible Acts

EXAMPLE 4

While Bertha is at the tuck shop replenishing her somewhat depleted sweetie store Bill revises the game. Bertha has a further choice of the colour green and the pay-offs shown in Table 6.6 apply.

Table 6.6

		Bertha		
		Pink	White	Green
Bill	Pink	7	−3	4
	White	1	6	0

The game has no saddle point and the players must derive their mixed strategies.

Bertha realises that the pay-off (to Bill) is always lower when she selects green than if she chooses pink. Choosing pink involves a greater loss to Bertha than choosing green and we say that choosing pink is an *inadmissible act* which Bertha eliminates.

Table 6.7

		Bertha	
		White	Green
Bill	Pink	−3	4
	White	6	0

Pay-offs in the reduced game are shown in Table 6.7. The mixed strategies are developed as in Example 3 and verification of the solution below is left as an exercise for the reader.

Bill's optimal mixed strategy is to choose pink with probability 6/13 and white with probability 7/13.

Bertha's optimal strategy is to choose white with probability 4/13 and green with probability 9/13.

The value of the game is 24/13 (to Bill).

Mixed Strategies for a 3 x 2 Game with no Saddle Point

EXAMPLE 5

As she is about to nod off to sleep, Bertha is disturbed by Bill who has yet another version of the colour game. The choices and the appropriate pay-offs are given in Table 6.8.

Table 6.8

| | | Bertha | |
		Pink	White
Bill	Pink	−3	4
	White	5	2
	Green	6	−3

Bill has a greater number of choices than Bertha but the analysis presented below effectively eliminates one of Bill's choices, and thus ensures that each player has an equal number of choices. We will show that Bertha adopts a strategy which effectively eliminates Bill's choice of green. Accordingly, we will consider Bertha's mixed strategy first.

Formulation of Expected Pay-off Equations

Bertha will select pink with probability q, white with probability $1 - q$, and we must find the value of q which will minimise Bertha's expected loss.

The analysis begins as in Example 3. Remember that Bertha's loss is equivalent to Bill's pay-off.

When Bill selects pink his expected pay-off = Bertha's expected loss
$$= -3q + 4(1 - q)$$
$$= -7q + 4 \qquad (5)$$

When Bill selects white his expected pay-off = Bertha's expected loss
$$= 5q + 2(1 - q)$$
$$= 3q + 2 \qquad (6)$$

When Bill selects green his expected pay-off = Bertha's expected loss
$$= 6q - 3(1 - q)$$
$$= 9q - 3 \qquad (7)$$

Solution of expected Pay-off Equations

Shown in Figure 6.3 are the graphs of $-7q + 4$, $3q + 2$ and $9q - 3$ as q varies over the interval $(0, 1)$.

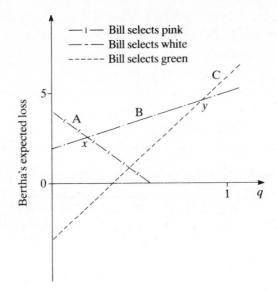

Figure 6.3

Notice that the lines which correspond to equations (5) and (6) intersect at the point $q = 1/5$. The lines corresponding to equations (6) and (7) intersect at $q = 5/6$ and the lines corresponding to equations (5) and (7) intersect at $q = 7/16$. These values can be read from Figure 6.3 or they can be derived more accurately by solving the equations in pairs, as in Example 3.

Let us turn our attention to the variation of Bill's expected pay-off as q takes values between 0 and 1. The pay-off can be read directly from Figure 6.3 or by substituting for q into equations (5), (6) and (7). This information is summarised in Table 6.9.

Table 6.9

Line	Range of q	Corresponding values of Bill's expected pay-off	Bill's optimal choice
A	(0, 1/5)	(4, 13/5)	Pink
B	(1/5, 5/6)	(13/5, 9/2)	White
C	(5/6, 1)	(9/2, 6)	Green

A, B and C are sections of the graphs of equations (5), (6) and 7), respectively. They correspond to Bill's optimal strategies over the range of q. If, for example, Bertha operates her mixed strategy with q in the interval (0, 1/5), Bill chooses pink rather than white or green. Figure 6.3 shows that a choice of pink guarantees Bill a higher expected pay-off than either of the alternatives.

A similar argument may be extended over the entire range of q and therefore consideration is given only to the line segments A, B, C and the points at which they intersect, x and y.

As in Example 3, Bertha chooses that value of q which gives the smallest pay-off to Bill, whatever his choice. At the intersection x, q is 1/5 and the corresponding expected pay-off is 13/5. At the intersection y, q is 5/6 and the corresponding expected pay off is 9/2. Choosing the alternative for which Bill's expected pay-off is smallest Bertha's optimal strategy is therefore to choose pink with probability 1/5 and white with probability 4/5.

We will now find Bill's mixed strategy.

Formulation of Expected Pay-off Equations

Bill has access to the same information as Bertha and understands that she will adopt the strategy we derived above. Therefore Bill would not choose green, for if he does so his expected pay-off (when Bertha is operating with $q = 1/5$) is lower than when he chooses pink or white (Figure 6.3). This may be verified algebraically by substituting $q = 1/5$ into each of the equations (5), (6) and (7) (corresponding to each of Bill's choices of pink, white and green). The resulting expected pay-offs (to Bill) are 13/5, 13/5 and $-6/5$ respectively.

Following the method described in Example 3, Bill's mixed strategy is therefore derived from the reduced Table 6.10.

Table 6.10

| | | Bertha | |
		Pink	White
Bill	Pink	−3	4
	White	5	2

The expected pay-off equations are found in terms of p, the probability of Bill choosing pink. These are then solved simultaneously and Bill's mixed strategy is to choose pink with probability $p = 3/10$ and white with probability 7/10.

The value of the game, found by substituting $p = 3/10$ into either (5) or (6), is 13/5 (to Bill).

Optimal Strategies

Bertha's optimal mixed strategy is to choose pink with probability 1/5 and white with probability 4/5.

Bill's optimal mixed strategy is to choose pink with probability 3/10 and white with probability 7/10.

The value of the game is 13/5 (to Bill).

Formulation of a Gaming Problem as a Linear Program

EXAMPLE 6

As an exercise for the whole class the decision maths teacher has devised a game to be played in pairs. One member of the pair is player A, the other is B, this allocation being made arbitrarily by the teacher. Each player has three choices and the following pay-offs apply.

Table 6.11

		Player B		
		B1	B2	B3
	A1	3	1	–10
Player A	A2	5	9	7
	A3	12	4	–3

There are no inadmissible acts and no saddle points. A neat solution to this more complex game can be found using linear programming methods.

The *decision variables* are the probabilities corresponding to the various choices each player has.

The *objective function* is the value of the game, which in this case is A's expected pay-off. Each player wishes to maximise his own pay-off.

The *constraints* are derived from the expected pay-off (to A) under each of B's choices.

As in the previous examples we develop each player's mixed strategy separately. Let us consider the player A.

Notation

First we must define the notation we are using.

Let p_i = the probability that A chooses act A_i (i = 1, 2, 3)

q_j = the probability that B chooses act B_j (j = 1, 2, 3)

v_{ij} = pay-off (to A) when A chooses A_i and B chooses B_j

V = value of the game (to A).

Objective

Each player wishes to make as much money as he can, he wants to maximise his expected pay-off. As in previous examples A's expected pay-off is the value of the game, V. The object is therefore to maximise V.

Constraints

Each constraint is expressed in terms of A's expected pay-off and there is one constraint for each of B's choices.

B chooses	A's expected pay–off
B_1	$3p_1 + 5p_2 + 12p_3$
B_2	$1p_1 + 9p_2 + 4p_3$
B_3	$-10p_1 + 7p_2 - 3p_3$

The value of the game (to A) is V. As yet it is undetermined but whatever its actual magnitude A's expected pay-off under each of B's choices must be at least as big as V. The following statements are therefore true:

$$3p_1 + 5p_2 + 12p_3 \geq V \tag{A1}$$

$$1p_1 + 9p_2 + 4p_3 \geq V \tag{A2}$$

$$-10p_1 + 7p_2 - 3p_3 \geq V \tag{A3}$$

Rearranging the inequalities (A1), (A2) and (A3),

$$V - 3p_1 - 5p_2 - 12p_3 \leq 0 \tag{A4}$$

$$V - 1p_1 - 9p_2 - 4p_3 \leq 0 \tag{A5}$$

$$V + 10p_1 - 7p_2 + 3p_3 \leq 0 \tag{A6}$$

The simplex algorithm operates with equations. Therefore we introduce the slack variables S_1, S_2, S_3 into the inequalities (A4), (A5) and (A6) respectively. This gives the following system of equations.

$$V - 3p_1 - 5p_2 - 12p_3 + S_1 = 0$$

$$V - 1p_1 - 9p_2 - 4p_3 + S_2 = 0$$

$$V + 10p_1 - 7p_2 + 3p_3 + S_3 = 0$$

There are two further constraints. The first is

$$p_1 + p_2 + p_3 = 1 \tag{A7}$$

which is necessary to satisfy basic probability rules. In accordance with the requirement of the simplex algorithm that an artificial variable, a say, must be incorporated into constraints which are equalities, equation A7 is rewritten as

$$p_1 + p_2 + p_3 + a = 1$$

Finally, there is the usual non-negativity constraint

$$a, p_1, p_2, p_3, S_1, S_2, S_3 \geq 0$$

Note that V is unconstrained here; since it is the value of the game (to A); it may take negative values when A loses to B.

The complete program is

maximise V

subject to
$$V - 3p_1 - 5p_2 - 12p_3 + S_1 = 0$$
$$V - 1p_1 - 9p_2 - 4p_3 + S_2 = 0$$
$$V + 10p_1 - 7p_2 + 3p_3 + S_3 = 0$$
$$p_1 + p_2 + p_3 + a = 1$$
$$a, p_1, p_2, p_3, S_1, S_2, S_3 \geq 0$$

This linear program can be solved using the Simplex method. A's mixed strategy is to choose A1 with probability $p_1 = 22/81$, A2 with probability $p_2 = 43/81$ and A3 with probability $p_3 = 16/81$. A's expected pay-off, which is also the value of the game is, 473/81 (to A).

Exercises

6.1 Determine A's maximin pay-off strategy and associated pay-off (to A) in each of the following games:

(i)

	B1	B2
A1	6	9
A2	5	7

(ii)

	B1	B2
A1	3	2
A2	-1	-4

(iii)

	B1	B2
A1	-1	3
A2	-7	-5

6.2 Find D's minimax loss strategy and his associated pay-off (expressed in terms of C's pay-off) in each of the following games:

(i)

	D1	D2
C1	-3	-9
C2	3	5

(ii)

	D1	D2
C1	− 6	−5
C2	− 9	−7

(iii)

	D1	D2
C1	1	7
C2	−7	5

6.3   Compare A's maximin pay-off strategy found in Exercise 6.1(i) and D's minimax – loss strategy found in Exercise 6.2(ii). Comment.

6.4   Find the saddle point and value of each of the games in Exercise 6.1.

6.5   Determine the saddle point value (to A) of the following game:

	B1	B2
A1	3	1
A2	4	−9

6.6   Find the equilibrium act pair and the value (to A) of the following games:

(i)

	B1	B2	B3
A1	2	7	3
A2	0	5	2

(ii)

	B1	B2	B3	B4	B5
A1	5	4	2	0	5
A2	7	1	−9	−2	1

(iii)

	B1	B2	B3
A1	3	5	2
A2	4	1	5

(iv)

	B1	B2	B3	B4
A1	−3	0	−7	1
A2	1	6	0	2

(v)

	B1	B2	B3	B4	B5
A1	1	6	2	9	1
A2	5	10	5	12	5

6.7   Find the optimal mixed strategies for the following games:

(i)

	B1	B2
A1	-7	2
A2	1	-5

(ii)

	B1	B2
A1	9	-3
A2	0	5

(iii)

	B1	B2
A1	5	-2
A2	-8	6

(iv)

	B1	B2
A1	-6	5
A2	9	-7

6.8   Which of the acts in the following games would the players consider to be inadmissible?

(i)

	B1	B2	B3
A1	5	7	3
A2	7	9	12
A3	13	1	4

(ii)

	B1	B2	B3
A1	5	-4	5
A2	6	2	3
A3	-2	-5	4

(iii)

	B1	B2
A1	3	4
A2	9	-3
A3	2	7
A4	6	9

Appendix 1

Introduction to Probability

Suppose that in a given situation we know that just one of finitely many possible events will occur, but we do not know which one. To show that some events are more (or less) likely to occur than others we introduce the idea of probability. The probability of an event is a number between 0 and 1.

If the probability is 0, the event will never happen i.e. it is an impossibility. If the probability is 1 the event will always happen i.e. it is a certainty. Probabilities between 0 and 1 show that sometimes the event will happen and sometimes it will not. Consider the event 'A 4 is thrown with a fair die'. Since there are 6 possible events, all equally likely, then the probability of the event occurring is 1/6. The probability of the event not occurring is 5/6. If we threw a die many many times then on average a 4 would be thrown one sixth of the time. Notice that if we add the probabilities of all possible events they sum to 1.

What is the probability of throwing an even number? There are 3 even numbers and 3 odd numbers, so the probability of throwing an even number is 0.5; the same as throwing an odd number.

As a further example, consider a pack of cards, comprising the usual spades, clubs, diamonds and hearts and 1 joker, 53 cards in all.

The probability of drawing a club = 13/53.
The probability of drawing a jack = 4/53.
The probability of drawing a joker = 1/53.

We are 4 times more likely to draw a jack than a joker.

Accordingly, if we say that the probability of a certain event occurring is p then p will denote a number anywhere in the range from 0 to 1, inclusive; the value $p = 1$ indicates that the event is certain to happen, while the value $p = 0$ indicates that it is certain not to happen. If p is the probability that the event will happen then $1 - p$ is the probability the event will not happen. In Example 3 Bill has precisely two courses of action, namely the choice of pink or the choice of white. If p is the probability that he chooses pink then $1 - p$ is the probability that he does not choose pink i.e. that he chooses white.

Appendix 2

Expected Value

Expected value is defined by:

$$\text{Expected value} = \sum(\text{prob of an event}) \cdot (\text{value of the event})$$

Consider again the fair die, with faces numbered 1, 2, 3, 4, 5, 6. These are the 6 possible events. All events have the same probability of 1/6.

$$\text{Expected value of a throw} = \frac{1}{6}(1) + \frac{1}{6}(2) + \frac{1}{6}(3) + \frac{1}{6}(4) + \frac{1}{6}(5) + \frac{1}{6}(6) = 3.5$$

If you threw a die several times, noting the number thrown each time, the average number would be 3.5.

Suppose a gambler fixed the die so the probability of throwing a 6 was 0.4, the probability of throwing a 5 was 0.2 and 4, 3, 2, and 1 had equal probabilities. What is the expected value?

Probability of throwing a 6 = 0.4
Probability of throwing a 5 = 0.2

The probability of throwing a 1, 2, 3 or 4 is $1 - [0.4 + 0.2] = 0.4$
These events have equal probability so:

Probability of throwing a 1 = 0.1
Probability of throwing a 2 = 0.1
Probability of throwing a 3 = 0.1
Probability of throwing a 4 = 0.1

The expected value =

$$0.1(1) + 0.1(2) + 0.1(3) + 0.1(4) + 0.2(5) + 0.4(6) = 4.4$$

7

SOLUTIONS TO EXERCISES

Chapter 1

1.1   The inputs are the name to be searched (NOM) and the list of names. The output is the position of the name in the list.

1.2
Step 1   Note the name to be found.
Step 2   Starting with the first entry and continuing down the list read each entry to see if it is the given name. Note any positions where the name is found.
Step 3   If the name is not found note the result 'Name not in list'.

The algorithm may also be written as:
1.   Input name to be searched; NOM
2. $J = N + 1$
3.   For $I = 1$ to N
4.   If $NAME(I) = NOM$ then print 'Position of NOM is', I and set $J = I$
5.   Next I
6.   If $J \leq N$ then goto 7 else print 'Name not in list'
7.   STOP.

1.3(a)   The list contains 11 names.

$$A \; B \; C \; D \; E \; F \; G \; H \; I \; J \; K$$

1st. application
Look at the middle name (i.e. F) and assume the given name is not there. The two lists on either side both contain 5 names. Assume for the sake of argument the first list is now examined.

2nd. application $A \; B \; C \; D \; E$

Look at the middle name (i.e. C). The given name is not there. The two remaining lists both contain 2 names. Assume that the first list is examined.

3rd. application $A \; B$

Look at the middle name (i.e. B). The given name is not there.

4th. application   A

The list is now just a single name and examination will reveal if it is or is not the given name.

A maximum of 4 applications of the binary search algorithm is needed.

1.3(b)   The list contains 12 names.

A B C D E F G H I J K L

1st. application
Examine the middle name (i.e. G). This is not the given name. The longer list is examined.

2nd. application   A B C D E F

Examine the middle name (D). This is not the given name and the longer list is considered.

3rd. application   A B C

The middle name is B and this is examined. It is not the given name. For the sake of argument assume the first list is examined.

4th. application   A

This fourth application will decide whether or not the given name is contained in the list.

A maximum of 4 applications of the binary search algorithm is needed.

1.4(a)   Sequential search
In the worst possible case all N names will be examined.

1.4(b)   Binary search
The list contains N names.
After the 1st. application the maximum length of a remaining list is $[N/2]$.
After the 2nd. application the maximum length of a remaining list is $[N/2^2]$.
After the rth. application the maximum length of a remaining list is $[N/2^r]$.

Hence there can be at most r applications of the algorithm where r is the smallest number such that $2^r > N$.

1.5(a)   The 'worst case' possible for the bubblesort algorithm occurs when the list of numbers is in decreasing order. In such a case only one number will be correctly positioned with each application of the algorithm. So for a list containing 6 numbers at most 5 applications of the algorithm are necessary.

1.5(b)   In the first application 5 pairs of numbers are compared. In the second application 4 pairs of numbers are compared and so on. The total number of pairs compared is 15 (i.e. $5 + 4 + 3 + 2 + 1$).

1.6   We compare the bubblesort algorithm given in the text (alg 1) and the simplified algorithm given in the question (alg 2).

Alg 1 contains a counter (R) which counts the number of times numbers have been interchanged. If during an application of alg 1, $R = 0$ then no numbers have been interchanged and so all numbers must be in ascending order. Hence the algorithm ceases.

In alg 2, no such counter exists. Even if no numbers are interchanged during an application the algorithm still continues to the next application. This is done until the last application when only one pair of numbers is considered.

In summary, alg 2 cannot detect when the list is in ascending order. Alg 1 can and so an early exit from the algorithm is possible.

Alg 1 is more efficient since fewer applications will be needed to order a list.

1.7   We are given a list of N unordered numbers, a(1), a(2), . . . , a(N). We could simply use the bubblesort algorithm and then read the first (smallest) and last (largest) numbers. An alternative to find both the smallest and largest numbers is as follows.

Step 1   Set numbers S and L both equal to the first number in the list, a(1).
Step 2   If a(2) is smaller than a(1), set S = a(2). If a(2) is larger than a(1), set L = a(2).
Step 3   Repeat step 2 for a(3), a(4), . . . , a(N).
Step 4   The smallest number is S, the largest number is L.

In programming style, the algorithm is:
1.   Set S = a(1), L = a(1)
2.   For i = 2 to N
3.   If a(i) < S then S = a(i). If a(i) > L then L = a(i)
4.   Next i
5.   S = smallest number in the list, L = largest number in the list.

1.8(a)   5 4 3 2 1 0

1st. application
Interchange 1, 0   5 4 3 2 0 1
Interchange 2, 0   5 4 3 0 2 1
Interchange 3, 0   5 4 0 3 2 1
Interchange 4, 0   5 0 4 3 2 1
Interchange 5, 0   0 5 4 3 2 1

2nd. application
Interchange 2, 1   0 5 4 3 1 2
Interchange 3, 1   0 5 4 1 3 2
Interchange 4, 1   0 5 1 4 3 2
Interchange 5, 1   0 1 5 4 3 2

3rd. application
Interchange 3, 2   0 1 5 4 2 3
Interchange 4, 2   0 1 5 2 4 3
Interchange 5, 2   0 1 2 5 4 3

4th. application
Interchange 4, 3   0 1 2 5 3 4
Interchange 5, 3   0 1 2 3 5 4

5th. application
Interchange 5, 4   0 1 2 3 4 5

1.8(b)

6 9 –3 4 –17

1st. application

Interchange 4, –17	6 9 –3 –17 4
Interchange –3, –17	6 9 –17 –3 4
Interchange 9 –17	6 –17 9 –3 4
Interchange 6, –17	–17 6 9 –3 4

2nd. application

No interchange needed for –3, 4	–17 6 9 –3 4
Interchange 9, –3	–17 6 –3 9 4
Interchange 6, –3	–17 –3 6 9 4

3rd. application

Interchange 9, 4	–17 –3 6 4 9
Interchange 6, 4	–17 –3 4 6 9

4th. application

No interchange needed for 6, 9	–17 –3 4 6 9

1.9(a)

5 4 3 2 1 0

1st. application

Interchange 5, 4	4 5 3 2 1 0

2nd. application

Interchange 5, 3	4 3 5 2 1 0
Interchange 4, 3	3 4 5 2 1 0

3rd. appliction

Interchange 5, 2	3 4 2 5 1 0
Interchange 4, 2	3 2 4 5 1 0
Interchange 3, 2	2 3 4 5 1 0

4th. application

Interchange 5, 1	2 3 4 1 5 0
Interchange 4, 1	2 3 1 4 5 0
Interchange 3, 1	2 1 3 4 5 0
Interchange 1, 2	1 2 3 4 5 0

5th. application

Interchange 5, 0	1 2 3 4 0 5
Interchange 4, 0	1 2 3 0 4 5
Interchange 3, 0	1 2 0 3 4 5
Interchange 2, 0	1 0 2 3 4 5
Interchange 1, 0	0 1 2 3 4 5

1.9(b)   6 9 –3 4 –17

1st. application
No interchange needed for 6, 9

2nd. application
Interchange 9, –3   6 –3 9 4 –17
Interchange 6, –3   –3 6 9 4 –17

3rd. application
Interchange 9, 4   –3 6 4 9 –17
Interchange 6, 4   –3 4 6 9 –17

No interchange necessary for –3, 4

4th. application
Interchange 9, –17   –3 4 6 –17 9
Interchange 6, –17   –3 4 –17 6 9
Interchange 4, –17   –3 –17 4 6 9
Interchange –3, –17   –17 –3 4 6 9

1.10   9 4 12 21 14 6 10 6 3 12

Choose the number at the mid-point of the list i.e. 6. L_1 is the list of all numbers smaller than 6, L_2 is the list of all numbers greater than or equal to 6.

$$4 \;\; 3 \;\; 6 \;\; 9 \;\; 12 \;\; 21 \;\; 14 \;\; 10 \;\; 6 \;\; 12$$
$$\underbrace{}_{L_1} \qquad \underbrace{}_{L_2}$$

Applying quicksort to L_1 yields 3 4.

Consider L_2 9 12 21 14 10 6 12

Choose a number at the mid-point i.e. 14 and produce lists L_3 and L_4

$$9 \;\; 12 \;\; 10 \;\; 6 \;\; 12 \;\; 14 \;\; 21$$
$$\underbrace{}_{L_3} \qquad \underbrace{}_{L_4}$$

The full list is now

$$3 \;\; 4 \;\; 6 \;\; 9 \;\; 12 \;\; 10 \;\; 6 \;\; 12 \;\; 14 \;\; 21$$
$$\underbrace{}_{L_3}$$

Since L_4 comprises only 1 number no further applications are needed to this list. Consider then L_3

                          9 12 10 6 12

Application of the quicksort algorithm yields

$$9 \; 6 \; 10 \; 12 \; 12$$

$$\underbrace{}_{L_5} \quad \underbrace{}_{L_6}$$

The full list is now

$$3 \; 4 \; 6 \; 9 \; 6 \; 10 \; 12 \; 12 \; 14 \; 21$$

$$\underbrace{}_{L_5} \quad \underbrace{}_{L_6}$$

Applying quicksort to L_5 and L_6 completes the problem.

$$3 \; 4 \; 6 \; 6 \; 9 \; 10 \; 12 \; 12 \; 14 \; 21$$

Chapter 2

2.1 *Initial solution*

	M	N
A	3	
B	1	2
C		6

First iteration
Cost of initial solution £43
Source costs for A, B, C are 0, 7, 11 respectively.
Destination costs for M, N are 1, – 6 respectively.

Route	AN	CM
Saving	–13	3

Entering square CM

Adjustment sequence	CM	CN	BN	BM
	+	–	+	–

Adjustment quantity 1
Exiting square BM

Second iteration

	M	N
A	3	
B		3
C	1	5

Cost of current solution £40
Source costs for A, B, C are 0, 4, 8 respectively.
Destination costs for M, N are 1, –3 respectively.

Route	AN	BM
Saving	–10	–3

Current solution optimal

2.2 *Initial solution*

	C	D
A	4	1
B		7

First iteration
Cost of initial solution £45
Source costs for A, B are 0, −1 respectively.
Destination costs for C, D are 9, 2 respectively.
Route   BC
Saving   1
Entering square BC

Adjustment sequence	BC	BD	AD	AC
	+	−	+	−

Adjustment quantity 4
Exiting square AC

Second iteration

		C	D
A			5
B		4	3

Cost of current solution £41
Source costs for A, B are 0, −1 respectively.
Destination costs for C, D are 8, 2 respectively.
Route   AC
Saving   −1
Current solution optimal

2.3 *Initial solution*

	H	I	J	K
U	5			
V	2	8	2	
W			1	6

First iteration
Cost of initial solution £84
Source costs for U, V, W are 0, 3, 7 respectively.
Destination costs for H, I, J, K are 3, 1, 0, −5 respectively.

Route	UI	UJ	UK	VK	WH	WI
Saving	−5	−7	−7	−4	8	−2

Entering square WH

Adjustment sequence	WH	WJ	VJ	VH
	+	−	+	−

Adjustment quantity 1
Exiting square WJ

Second iteration

	H	I	J	K
U	5			
V	1	8	3	
W	1			6

Cost of current solution £76
Source costs for U, V, W are 0, 3, −1 respectively.
Destination costs for H, I, J, K are 3, 1, 0, 3 respectively.

Route	UI	UJ	UK	VK	WI	WJ
Saving	−5	−7	1	4	−10	−8

Entering square VK

Adjustment sequence	VK	WK	WH	VH
	+	−	+	−

Adjustment quantity 1
Exiting square VH

Third iteration

	H	I	J	K
U	5			
V		8	3	1
W	2			5

Cost of current solution £72
Source costs for U, V, W are 0, −1, −1 respectively.
Destination costs for H, I, J, K are 3, 5, 4, 3 respectively.

Route	UI	UJ	UK	VH	WI	WJ
Saving	−1	−3	1	−4	−6	−4

Entering square UK

Adjustment sequence	UK	WK	WH	UH
	+	−	+	−

Adjustment quantity 5
WK and UH tie for exiting square. The tie is broken arbitrarily. If UH is chosen the solution proceeds as follows.

Fourth iteration

	H	I	J	K
U				5
V		8	3	1
W	7			0

Cost of current solution £67
Source costs for U, V, W are 0, 0, 0 respectively.
Destination costs for H, I, J, K are 2, 4, 3, 2 respectively.

Route	UH	UI	UJ	VH	WI	WJ
Saving	−1	−2	−4	−4	−6	−4

Current solution optimal

2.4 *Initial solution*

	M	N
A	3	
B	3	2
C		2

First iteration
Cost of initial solution £44
Source costs for A, B, C are 0, 0, 2 respectively.
Destination costs for M, N are 2, 7 respectively.

Route	AN	CM
Saving	1	−2

Entering square AN

Adjustment sequence	AN	BN	BM	AM
	+	−	+	−

Adjustment quantity 2
Exiting square BN

Second iteration

	M	N
A	1	2
B	5	
C		2

Cost of current solution £42
Source costs for A, B, C are 0, 0, 3 respectively.
Destination costs for M, N are 2, 6 respectively.

Route	BN	CM
Saving	−1	−1

Current solution optimal

2.5   First Option

Initial solution

	D	E	F
A	5	3	
B		5	1
C			5

First iteration
Cost of initial solution £69.
Source costs for A, B, C are 0, 1, 1 respectively.
Destination costs for D, E, F are 2, 3, 4 respectively.

Route	AF	BD	CD	CE
Saving	3	−1	1	−5

Entering square AF

Adjustment sequence	AF	AE	BE	BF
	+	−	+	−

Adjustment quantity 1
Exiting square BF

Second iteration

	D	E	F
A	5	2	1
B		6	
C			5

Cost of current solution £66
Source costs for A, B, C are 0, 1, 4 respectively.
Destination costs for D, E, F are 2, 3, 1 respectively.

Route	BD	BF	CD	CE
Saving	−1	−3	4	−2

Entering square CD

Adjustment sequence	CD	CF	AF	AD
	+	−	+	−

Adjustment quantity 5

AD and CF tie for exiting square and this may be broken arbitrarily. If AD is chosen the solution proceeds as follows.

Third iteration

	D	E	F
A		2	6
B		6	
C	5		0

Cost of current solution £46
Source costs for A, B, C are 0, 1, 4 respectively.
Destination costs for D, E, F are −2, 3, 1 respectively.

Route	AD	BD	BF	CE
Saving	− 4	−5	−3	−2

Current solution optimal.

2.5 Second Option

Working with respect to time, which will later be used to assess the total cost of the distribution schedule.

Initial solution

	D	E	F
A	5	3	
B		5	1
C			5

First iteration

Time taken in initial solution 120 hours.
Source times for A, B, C are 0, 2, 5 respectively.
Destination times for D, E, F are 7, 6, 0 respectively.

Route	AF	BD	CD	CE
Saving	−9	1	7	5

Entering square CD

Adjustment sequence	CD	CF	BF	BE	AE	AD
	+	−	+	−	+	−

Adjustment quantity 5

Exiting square: tie between AD, BE and CF which may be broken arbitrarily. If CF is chosen the solution proceeds as follows.

Second iteration

	D	E	F
A	0	8	
B		0	6
C	5		

Time of current solution 85 hours
Source times for A, B, C are 0, 2, –2 respectively.
Destination times for D, E, F are 7, 6, 0 respectively.

Route	AF	BD	CE	CF
Saving	–9	1	–2	–7

Entering square BD

Adjustment sequence	BD	BE	AE	AD
	+	–	+	–

Adjustment quantity 0

AD and BE tie for exiting square. If BE is chosen the solution proceeds as follows.

Third iteration

	D	E	F
A	0	8	
B	0		6
C	5		

Time of current solution is once again 85 hours, since the only change has involved an empty square.
Source times for A, B, C are 0, 1, –2 respectively.
Destination times for D, E, F are 7, 6, 1 respectively.

Route	AF	BE	CE	CF
Saving	– 8	–1	–2	– 6

Current solution optimal.

The cost of the second option is $0.5 \times 85 = £42.50$. Since this is less than the cost of the first option (£46) the contractor should employ another firm to deliver the goods.

Chapter 3

3.1

		Task			
		H	P	W	
	D	2	6	7	2
Individual	E	8	1	9	1
	F	6	1	8	1
Deductions					4

		Task			
		H	P	W	
	D	0	4	5	
Individual	E	7	0	8	
	F	5	0	7	
Deductions		0	0	5	5

		Task		
		H	P	W
	D	0	4	0
Individual	E	7	0	3
	F	5	0	2

		Task		
		H	P	W
	D	0	6	0
Individual	E	5	0	1
	F	3	0	0

Individual	Task	Time to complete task
D	H	2
E	P	1
F	W	8
Total time to complete tasks		11 minutes

3.2

		Task					
		A	B	C	D	E	
	H	2	5	9	1	4	1
	I	4	2	1	3	9	1
Individual	J	3	2	5	5	8	2
	K	4	8	6	4	2	2
	L	3	9	4	1	7	1
Deductions							7

		Task				
		A	B	C	D	E
Individual	H	1	4	8	0	3
	I	3	1	0	2	8
	J	1	0	3	3	6
	K	2	6	4	2	0
	L	2	8	3	0	6
Deductions		1	0	0	0	0	1

		Task				
		A	B	C	D	E
Individual	H	0	4	8	0	3
	I	2	1	0	2	8
	J	0	0	3	3	6
	K	1	6	4	2	0
	L	1	8	3	0	6

Individual	Task	Time to complete tasks
H	A	2
I	C	1
J	B	2
K	E	2
L	D	1
Total time to complete tasks		8 hours

3.3

		Task			
		L	M	N	
Individual	A	50	30	60	30
	B	30	40	50	30
	C	30	60	40	30
Deductions					90

		Task			
		L	M	N	
Individual	A	20	0	30	
	B	0	0	20	
	C	0	30	10	
Deductions		0	0	10	

| | | Task | | |
		L	M	N
Individual	A	20	0	20
	B	0	10	10
	C	0	30	0

Individual	Task	Time to complete tasks
A	M	30
B	L	30
C	N	40
Total time to complete tasks		100 minutes

3.4

| | | Task | | | |
		M	S	O	
Individual	F	−50	−30	− 60	− 60
	G	−30	− 40	−50	− 50
	H	−30	− 60	− 40	− 60
Deductions					−170

| | | Task | | | |
		M	S	O	
Individual	F	10	30	0	
	G	20	10	0	
	H	30	0	20	
Deductions		10	0	0	10

| | | Task | | | |
		M	S	O	
Individual	F	0	30	0	
	G	10	10	0	
	H	20	0	20	
Deductions		10	0	0	10

Individual	Task	Time to complete tasks
F	M	50
G	O	50
H	S	60
Total time to complete tasks		160 minutes

The allocation of individuals to tasks which maximises (the negative) of an objective is not the same as the allocation which minimises the original objective.

3.5

		Task A	B	C	
Individual	L	50	30	30	30
	M	30	40	60	30
	N	60	60	40	40
Deductions					100

		Task A	B	C
Individual	L	20	0	0
	M	0	10	30
	N	20	20	0
Deductions		0	0	0

Individual	Task	Time to complete tasks
L	B	30
M	A	30
N	C	40
Total time to complete tasks		100 minutes

The presentation of the matrix of data is immaterial; whichever way up the information is presented the same optimal allocation is reached.

Chapter 4

4.1(i)

(a) $2 + 3 = 5$ hence the slack is $5 - 5 = 0$

(b) $4 + 12 = 16$ hence the slack is $17 - 16 = 1$

(c) $2 + 9 = 11$ hence the surplus is $11 - 10 = 1$

(d) surplus $= 0$

4.1(ii)

(a) $0.1(100) - 0.2(50) = 0$ hence the surplus is $0 - 0 = 0$

(b) $100 + 3(50) = 250$ hence the slack is $500 - 250 = 250$

(c) $10(100) + 30(50) = 2500$ hence the slack is $3500 - 2500 = 1000$

4.1(iii)

(a) $92 + 41 = 133$ hence the slack is $150 - 133 = 17$

(b)   surplus is $92 - 50 = 42$

(c)   slack is $50 - 41 = 9$

(d) $92 - 41 = 51$ surplus is $51 - 0 = 51$

4.2   Unless stated otherwise the feasible region is the shaded area in each diagram.

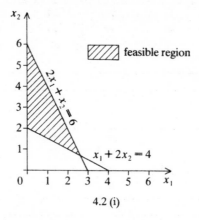

4.2 (i)

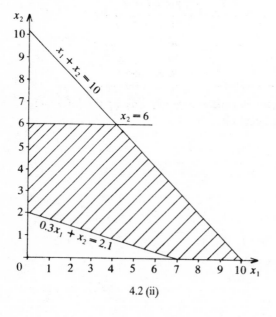

4.2 (ii)

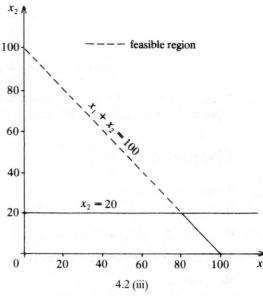

4.2 (iii)

4.3(i) $x_1 = 2$, $x_2 = 7.5$, $P = 9.5$

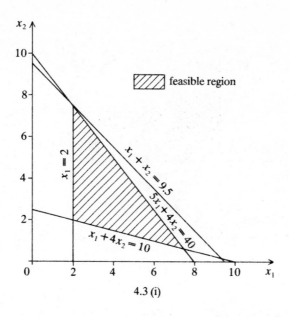

4.3 (i)

4.3(ii) $x_1 = 0$, $x_2 = 200$, $P = 400$

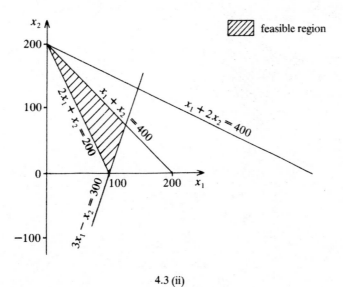

4.3 (ii)

4.3(iii) $x_1 = 4$, $x_2 = 6$, $C = 14$

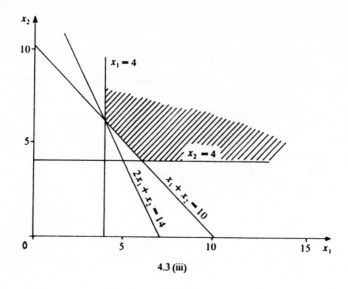

4.3 (iii)

4.3(iv) $x_1 = 500/3$, $x_2 = 100$, $C = 1300/3$

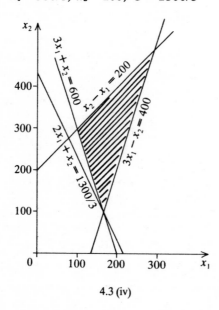

4.3 (iv)

4.4(i)   Linear program is:

Let x_M = number of Modern Miss dresses

x_D = number of Young Designer dresses

Maximise $P = 15x_M + 40x_D$

subject to $x_M + 2x_D \leq 40$ (sewing time constraint)

$3x_M + 3x_D \leq 90$ (fabric constraint)

$x_M,\ x_D \geq 0$ (non-negativity constraint)

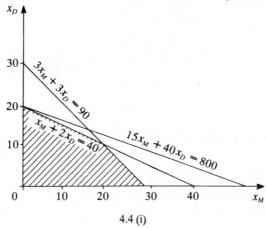

4.4 (i)

Buttons and Bows should make no Modern Miss dresses and 20 Young Designer dresses.

Sewing time used $= 0 + 2(20) = 40$ hours, hence there is no slack associated with this constraint.

Fabric used $= 3(0) + 3(20) = 60$m, hence there are $90 - 60 = 30$m fabric remain.

Profit $= 15(0) + 40(20) = £800$

4.4(ii)   Cuthbert spends £5 on his suitcase leaving $£80 - £5 = £75$ to buy stock.

Linear program is:

Let x_P = number of bottles of perfume

x_V = number of vases

Maximise $P = 0.2x_P + 0.3x_V$

subject to $0.75x_P + x_V \leq 75$ (financial constraint)

$x_P \geq 20$ (Cuthbert has to buy at least 20 bottles of perfume)

$0.2x_P + 0.4x_V \leq 20$ (weight constraint)

$x_P,\ x_V \geq 0$ (non-negativity constraint)

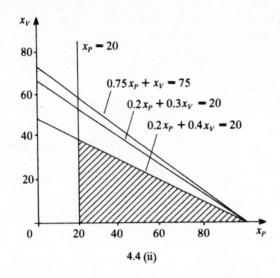

4.4 (ii)

Cuthbert should buy 100 bottles of perfume and no vases.

He spends $0.75(100) + 0 = £75$ and Cuthbert has no remaining capital.

Cuthbert was required to buy at least 20 bottles of perfume, hence there is a surplus of $100 - 20 = 80$ bottles associated with this constraint.

The total weight of his stock is $0.2(100) + 0 = 20$kgm and Cuthbert could carry no more.

The profit made $= 0.2(100) = £20$

Chapter 5

		x	y	z
5.1(i)	(a)	1	2	0
	(b)	6/7	10/7	1
	(c)	5/7	6/7	2
5.1(ii)	(a)	5	−5	0
	(b)	16/3	−11/3	1
	(c)	17/3	−7/3	2
5.1(iii)	(a)	−1	2	0
	(b)	−5/2	−3/4	1
	(c)	− 4	−7/2	2

	p	q	r	s
5.2(i)	3	1	0	0
5.2(ii)	20/9	8/9	1	1
5.2(iii)	13/9	7/9	2	2

5.3(i)

x_M = number of Modern Miss dresses

x_D = number of Young Designer dresses

x_S = slack associated with the sewing time constraint

x_F = slack associated with the fabric constraint

maximise	$P = 15x_M + 40x_D + 0x_S + 0x_F$	(objective function)
subject to	$x_M + 2x_D + x_S + 0x_F = 40$	(sewing time constraint)
	$3x_M + 3x_D + 0x_S + x_F = 90$	(fabric constraint)
	$x_M,\ x_D,\ x_S,\ x_F \geq 0$	(non-negativity constraint)

Tableau 1

basic variables	x_M	x_D	x_S	x_F	solution quantity b	row	ratio b/c
x_S	1	2	1	0	40	1	40/2 = 20
x_F	3	3	0	1	90	2	90/3 = 30
P	15	40	0	0	0	3	

The largest positive quantity in the objective function row is 40. The new basic variable is x_D.

The smallest possible ratio of b/c is 20. The exiting variable is therefore x_S.

Tableau 2

basic variables	x_M	x_D	x_S	x_F	solution quantity b	row	ratio b/c
x_D	1/2	1	1/2	0	20	4	
x_F	3/2	0	−3/2	0	30	5	
P	−5	0	−20	0	− 800	6	

There are no positive quantities in the objective function row and this solution is optimal.

$$x_D = 20 \quad x_F = 30 \quad x_M = 0 \quad x_S = 0 \quad P = £800$$

5.3(ii) x_P = number of bottles of perfume to be bought

x_V = number of vases to be bought

x_D = surplus associated with the demand constraint

a_D = artificial surplus associated with the demand constraint

x_C = slack associated with the cost constraint

x_W = slack associated with the weight constraint

maximise $P = 0.2x_P + 0.3x_V + 0x_D - ma_D + 0x_C + 0x_W$

subject to

$$x_P + 0x_V - 1x_D + 1a_D + 0x_C + 0x_W = 20 \qquad \text{(demand constraint)}$$
$$0.75x_P + 1x_V + 0x_D + 0a_D + 1x_C + 0x_W = 75 \qquad \text{(cost constraint)}$$
$$0.2x_P + 0.4x_V + 0x_D + 0a_D + 0x_C + 1x_W = 20 \qquad \text{(weight constraint)}$$
$$x_P, \ x_V, \ x_D, \ a_D, \ x_C, \ x_W \geq 0 \qquad \text{(non-negativity constraint)}$$

Tableau 1

basic variables	x_P	x_V	x_D	a_D	x_C	x_W	solution quantity b	row	ratio b/c
a_D	1	0	−1	1	0	0	20	1	
x_C	3/4	1	0	0	1	0	75	2	75
x_W	1/5	2/5	0	0	0	1	20	3	50
P	1/5	3/10	0	0	0	0	0	4	

Tableau 2

basic variables	x_P	x_V	x_D	a_D	x_C	x_W	solution quantity b	row	ratio b/c
a_D	1	0	−1	1	0	0	20	1	20
x_C	1/4	0	0	0	1	−5/2	25	6	100
x_V	1/2	1	0	0	0	5/2	50	5	100
P	1/20	0	0	−m	0	−3/4	−15	7	

Tableau 3

basic variables	x_P	x_V	x_D	a_D	x_C	x_W	solution quantity b	row	ratio b/c
x_P	1	0	−1	1	0	0	20	8	
x_C	0	0	1/4	−1/4	1	−5/2	20	9	80
x_V	0	1	1/2	−1/2	0	5/2	40	10	80
P	0	0	1/20	−m−1/20	0	−3/4	16	11	

Tableau 4

basic variables	x_P	x_V	x_D	a_D	x_C	x_W	solution quantity b	row
x_P	1	0	0	0	4	−10	100	13
x_D	0	0	1	−1	4	−10	80	14
x_V	0	1	0	0	−2	15/2	0	12
P	0	0	0	−m	−1/5	−1/4	−20	15

$x_P = 100 \quad x_D = 80 \quad x_V = 0 \quad P = 20$

x_D, the surplus associated with the minimum demand constraint is number of bottles of perfume – minimum demand = 100 – 20 = 80

The amount of capital invested $= 0.75x_P + 0x_V = 100(0.75) = 75$

Cuthbert has invested all of his capital and there is no surplus associated with this constraint i.e. $x_C = 0$

The weight constraint is also satisfied exactly and there is no slack associated with this constraint i.e. $x_W = 0$

$$x_P = 100 \ \ x_V = 0 \ \ x_D = 80 \ \ a_D = x_C = x_W = 0 \ \ P = £20$$

5.4
x_C = weight of cheesecake
x_M = weight of milk chocolate
x_T = weight of toffee
x_E = surplus associated with eating time constraint
x_K = slack associated with calorific constraint

maximise $\qquad P = 8x_C + 7x_M + 4x_T + 0x_E - ma_E + 0x_K$ (objective function)

subject to $\qquad 10x_C + 20x_M + 90x_T - 1x_E + 1a_E + 0x_K = 30$ (time constraint)

$300x_C + 600x_M + 500x_T + 0x_E + 0a_E + 1x_K = 1000$ (calorific constraint)

$x_C, \ x_M, \ x_T, \ x_E, \ a_E, \ x_K \geq 0$ (non-negativity constraint)

Tableau 1

basic variables	x_C	x_M	x_T	x_E	a_E	x_K	solution quantity b	row	ratio b/c
a_E	10	20	90	–1	1	0	30	1	3
x_K	300	600	500	0	0	1	1000	2	10/3
P	8	7	4	0	–m	0	0	3	

Tableau 2

basic variables	x_C	x_M	x_T	x_E	a_E	x_K	solution quantity b	row	ratio b/c
x_C	1	2	9	–1/10	1/10	0	3	4	
x_K	0	0	–2200	30	–30	1	100	5	10/3
P	0	–9	– 68	4/5	– 4/5–m	0	–24	6	

Tableau 3

basic variables	x_C	x_M	x_T	x_E	a_E	x_K	solution quantity b	row
x_C	1	2	5/3	0	0	1/300	10/3	7
x_E	0	0	–220/3	1	–1	1/30	10/3	8
P	0	–9	–28/3	0	–m	–2/75	– 80/3	9

There are no positive quantities in the objective function row and the current solution is optimal. Cuddles should eat $(10/3) \times 100$gram (i.e. 333 grams) of cheesecake. The slack associated with the calorific constraint is 10/3, all other variables are 0. Cuddles will enjoy 80/3 units of pleasure.

Chapter 6

6.1(i) A1 6   **(ii)** A1 2   **(iii)** A1 −1

6.2(i) D1 3   **(ii)** D1 −6   **(iii)** D1 1

6.3 A and B in (6.1)(i) correspond to D and C (respectively) in (6.2)(ii)

6.4(i) A1, B1 6 **(ii)** A1, B2 2   **(iii)** A1, B1 −1

6.5 B1 is inadmissible   A1, B2 is saddle-point   Value is 1 (to A)

6.6 **(i)** A1, B1 2   **(ii)** A1, B4 0
(iii)   no saddle-point, therefore no equilibrium pair
(iv) A2, B3 0   **(v)** A2, B1, A2, B5, and A2, B3 tie 5

6.7(i)
$$-7p + 1 - p = 2p - 5(1 - p)$$
$$-8p + 1 = 7p - 5$$
$$6 = 15p$$
$$p = 2/5$$

Therefore A should choose A1 with probability 2/5 and A2 with probability 3/5.

$$-7q + 2(1 - q) = q - 5(1 - q)$$
$$-9q + 2 = 6q - 5$$
$$7 = 15q$$
$$q = 7/15$$

Therefore B should choose B1 with probability 7/15 and B2 with probability 8/15.

Value is $7p - 5 = 7(2/5) - 5 = 14/5 - 25/5 = -11/5$ (to A)

6.7(ii)
$$9p = -3p + 5(1 - p)$$
$$9p = -8p + 5$$
$$17p = 5$$
$$p = 5/17$$

$$9q - 3(1 - q) = 5 - 5q$$
$$12q - 3 = 5 - 5q$$
$$17q = 8$$
$$q = 8/17$$

Value is $9p = 9(5/17) = 45/17$ (to A)

6.7(iii)

$$5p - 8(1 - p) = -2p + 6(1 - p)$$
$$13p - 8 = -8p + 6$$
$$21p = 14$$
$$p = 2/3$$

$$5q - 2(1 - q) = -8q + 6(1 - q)$$
$$7q - 2 = -14q + 6$$
$$21q = 8$$
$$q = 8/21$$

Value is $13p - 8 = 26/3 - 24/3 = 2/3$(toA)

6.7(iv)

$$-6p + 9(1 - p) = 5p - 7(1 - p)$$
$$-15p + 9 = 12p - 7$$
$$16 = 27p$$
$$p = 16/27$$

$$-6q + 5(1 - q) = 9q - 7(1 - q)$$
$$-11q + 5 = 16q - 7$$
$$12 = 27q$$
$$q = 4/9$$

Value is $-11q + 5 = -44/9 + 5 = 1/9$(toA)

6.8(i)

	B1	B2	B3
A1	5	7	3
A2	7	9	12
A3	13	1	4

A1 inadmissible

	B1	B2	B3
A2	7	9	12
A3	13	1	4

B3 inadmissible

	B1	B2
A1	7	9
A2	13	1

6.8(ii)

	B1	B2	B3
A1	5	-4	5
A2	6	2	3
A3	-2	-5	4

B1 inadmissible

	B2	B3
A1	−4	5
A2	2	3
A3	−5	4

B3 inadmissible

	B2
A1	−4
A2	2
A3	−5

A1, A3 inadmissible

6.8(iii)

	B1	B2
A1	3	4
A2	9	−3
A3	2	7
A4	6	9

A1 inadmissible

	B1	B2
A2	9	−3
A3	2	7
A4	6	9

A3 inadmissible

	B1	B2
A2	9	−3
A4	6	9